Contents

£2~25

6

7

8

Then...

ARRRGH!

OOPS!

IT...IT'S NOTHING. I'LL JUST GO AND BATHE THIS ELBOW!

ARE YOU HURT, VERA?

THE DOCTOR'S HERE LOOKING AT THAT MAN WHO WAS INJURED — I'LL GET HIM TO LOOK AT IT FOR YOU!

So...

HMM, NOTHING BROKEN, BUT YOU'LL HAVE TO REST IT COMPLETELY FOR A FEW DAYS...

WE'LL HAVE TO CANCEL THE PERFORMANCE — CAN'T RISK YOU BEING LAID-UP AFTERWARDS!

I'LL TAKE YOUR PLACE — NOBODY WOULD RECOGNISE ME IN COSTUME!

BUT I CAN'T — THE SHOW'S TOMORROW!

NO! LORD STANTON WOULD HAVE TO GIVE ALL THE MONEY BACK — THE KIDS' CHRISTMAS WOULD BE RUINED! THE SHOW MUST GO ON!

NO, I WON'T LET YOU, MOLLY! IT'S TOO DANGEROUS!

BUT YOU SAID YOU WOULDN'T BE DOING YOUR FULL ACT — AND I'M STRONGER THAN I LOOK, SO PLEASE!

After some discussion, Molly was given a "crash course" of instruction...

IT'S EITHER THAT, SIS — OR CALL THE SHOW OFF!

THAT'S IT, GRASP MY WRIST, TOO. IT'S CALLED A "BUTCHER'S GRIP" — SAFER THAN JUST GRIPPING WITH THE FINGERS!

9

11

BESSIE BUNTER

12

THE ONE WHO GOT AWAY

TURN LEFT HERE!

THIS IS SCAREY! PRISON WARDERS HAVEN'T WORN UNIFORMS LIKE THAT FOR DONKEYS YEARS! AND THAT CONVICT'S CLOTHES ARE OLD-FASHIONED, TOO.

WH-WHO ARE THEY? WHAT DO THEY WANT?

NOT FAR NOW.

BUT THIS ISN'T ANYWHERE NEAR WHERE THE PRISON IS — ER, WAS. LOOK, JUST WHAT'S GOING ON HERE?

BETTER PACK IT UP, NIGEL! WE'RE SCARING THE DAYLIGHTS OUT OF THESE GOOD PEOPLE.

I'M SORRY — JUST COULDN'T RESIST THE TEMPTATION! BUT HERE WE ARE!

WE WERE ON OUR WAY TO A FANCY-DRESS BALL AT THE CHIEF CONSTABLE'S WHEN OUR CAR BROKE DOWN!

WE TRAMPED ALONG, THEN WE SAW YOU, AND WE THOUGHT —

AND YOU THOUGHT WE WERE A PAIR OF MUGS YOU COULD SCARE THE PANTS OFF! WHY, I'LL —

DAD, PLEASE — DON'T LOSE YOUR TEMPER. IT-IT'S NOT WORTH IT!

YOU'RE RIGHT — IT WAS A JOKE IN POOR TASTE. LOOK, PERHAPS WE CAN MAKE IT UP TO YOU. WOULD YOU LIKE TO COME TO THE PARTY?

WELL — ER —

YES, WE'D LOVE TO!

And so later, when Sheena met the Chief Constable —

I'VE A GOOD MIND TO STICK THAT PAIR OF SCALLYWAGS IN A CELL FOR TONIGHT!

YEAH, FOR A WHILE WE THOUGHT THEY WERE GHOSTS.

GHOSTS, EH? NOW THAT'S STRANGE.

WHY?

WELL, ABOUT FIFTY YEARS AGO — ALMOST TO THE DAY, IN FACT — A PRISONER ESCAPED FROM FLEETMOOR. HE WAS THE ONLY ONE WHO WAS NEVER RECAUGHT.

SO HE GOT CLEAN AWAY? GOT HIS FREEDOM?

NO, I DON'T THINK SO. YOU SEE, A YEAR AFTER HIS ESCAPE, SOMEONE ELSE ADMITTED COMMITTING THE CRIME OUR ESCAPEE WAS PUT INSIDE FOR.

IF HE'D REALLY GOT AWAY, HE'D HAVE SHOWN UP FOR HIS PARDON. BUT HE NEVER DID, SO I RECKON HE LOST HIS LIFE TRYING TO CROSS THE MOORS.

HE GOT OFF TO A GOOD START, THOUGH — HITCHED A RIDE IN THE BACK OF A TRUCK.

A YOUNG GIRL SAW HIM GET IN THE TRUCK, BUT WHEN WE STOPPED IT, HE'D SCARPERED.

CRIKEY!

I-I SAW A CONVICT GET IN THE BACK OF DAD'S TRUCK! I-I'D ALMOST FORGOTTEN ABOUT HIM.

HEY, THERE HE IS! HIS FRIENDS MUST HAVE FORGOTTEN TO TELL HIM THEY'D ARRIVED AT THE PARTY.

BET YOUR FRIEND'S HOPPING MAD — HE'S JUST GOT OUT OF THE LORRY.

EH? WHAT ARE YOU TALKING ABOUT?

THE MAN I SAW GETTING OUT OF DAD'S LORRY JUST NOW! HE WAS IN FANCY-DRESS — A CONVICT'S OUTFIT JUST LIKE YOU'VE GOT ON!

B-BUT THERE **WERE** ONLY TWO OF US — WE DIDN'T COME WITH ANOTHER FRIEND.

B-BUT **WHO** DID I SEE, THEN?

PERHAPS IT WAS SIMPLY SOMEONE GATE-CRASHING THE PARTY. BUT I DON'T THINK SO — AND NEITHER DO YOU, DO YOU?

16

ANIMAL MAGIC

Tammy and Misty ☆ PUZZLES

PASTIME:
The name of a hobby many girls enjoy is shown here. Put the letters in the right order to name what it is.

ANSWER:
Embroidery.

CHAIN OF WORDS:
Make a chain of words with these objects. The last letter of each word should be the same as the first letter of the following one.

ANSWER:
Tap, palm, moth, half, fork, knife, eggs, seven, nail, leopard, dagger, rabbit.

CAKE PUZZLE:
If you put the word-pieces together correctly in pairs you will see six of the ingredients used in baking this delicious-looking cake!

ANSWER:
Almonds, sultanas, cherries, flour, butter, peel.

SQUARES:
Can you fit the numbers into the squares so that the total is 12 in every row, column and diagonal? To help you, we'll tell you that the centre figure is 4.

ANSWER:
Across: 3,8,1. 2,4,6. 7,0,5.

TRIANGLE:
In the 'star' sketch on the right are lots of triangles. How many can you find?

ANSWER:
Twenty.

CHARLIE'S NEIGHBOURS:
As he swings on the branches, Charlie the chimp can see six other animals. Find what they are by re-arranging each group of jumbled letters in the correct order.

ANSWER:
Leopard, antelope, buffalo, giraffe, rhinoceros, jaguar.

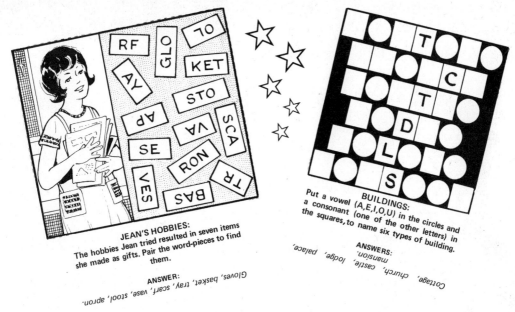

JEAN'S HOBBIES:
The hobbies Jean tried resulted in seven items she made as gifts. Pair the word-pieces to find them.

ANSWER:
Gloves, basket, tray, scarf, vase, stool, apron.

BUILDINGS:
Put a vowel (A,E,I,O,U) in the circles and a consonant (one of the other letters) in the squares, to name six types of building.

ANSWERS:
Cottage, church, castle, lodge, palace, mansion.

NAME THE ANIMAL:
The name of a zoo animal is hidden here. Unjumble the letters to find it.

ANSWER:
Hippopotamus.

FAMOUS MAN:
In the first picture, you can find the name of a profession. When you've done that, take the initial letters of the other objects to find the name of a man famous in that career.

ANSWER:
Historian — Carlyle.

BOTH THE SAME:
Two aprons are alike — but which?

ANSWER:
Nos. 3 and 6

WORDS AND PICTURES:
Pair the colours with the pictures to make six names or phrases.

ANSWER:
Blue Peter, Red Cross, Orange Blossom, Coral Island, Green Fingers, Black Sheep.

Wee Sue

Milltown School's visit to the pantomime was supposed to be a treat . . .

— AND I'D BE ENJOYING IT TOO, IF ONLY I COULD SEE IT!

OH, WELL PLAYED, SIR! A MOST APTLY-PLACED CUSTARD PIE!

TRUST YOU-KNOW-WHO TO BE WEARING THE HUGEST HAT IN TOWN — OUR VERY OWN UGLY SISTER!

OH WELL, HALF A PLAY IS BETTER THAN NONE, I S'POSE!

I'VE GOT A HATFUL OF SONGS TO SING YOU. . . .

AND NOW THE OTHER HALF. BUT IT'S KILLING MY NECK!

ER — COULDN'T YOU TAKE YOUR HAT OFF, TILL THE PANTO'S OVER, MISS BIGGER?

CERTAINLY NOT — I PAID FIVE POUNDS FOR THIS HAT AND I INTEND TO GET FULL VALUE OUT OF IT! NOW, SILENCE, GIRL — YOU ARE RUINING MY ENJOY-MENT WITH YOUR CEASELESS FIDGETING AND SHIFTING AROUND!

Afterwards, in the charabanc . . .

. . .I THINK I MAY SAFELY SAY THAT THANKS TO MY ARRANGEMENTS, WE ALL HAD A SPLENDID EVENING.

GOSH, YES, MISS BIGGER!

FOR SHE'S A JOLLY GOOD FELLOW.

NO NEED TO SING MY PRAISES, GIRLS, BUT DO CARRY ON!

HARK AT HER! SOON, EVEN THAT TEN-GALLON JOB'LL BE TOO SMALL FOR HER HEAD!

YOU'LL HAVE THE WHOLE WEEKEND IN WHICH TO WRITE A FINE ESSAY. THE SUBJECT IS — "THE PANTOMIME, AS I SAW IT!"

OOOH! NOW IF SHE'D ASKED ME TO WRITE ABOUT HATS — I'D BE BRIMMING WITH IDEAS!

HURRY ALONG, STRONG, AND GET IT DOWN — WHILE IT'S STILL FRESH IN YOUR FEEBLE BRAIN!

HUH! THE ONLY PANTO I'LL SEE WILL BE ON MONDAY WHEN I DON'T HAND IN AN ESSAY AND BIGGER PUTS A SLIPPER ON MY SEAT!

THIS SPOT'S GREAT. I CAN SEE THEM GETTING READY FOR THE NEXT SCENE THROUGH THERE. I NEVER REALISED WHAT WORK GOES ON BACKSTAGE!

ENJOYING IT, LUV? SILLY QUESTION — THE PANTO'S CAST ITS SPELL ON HER, RIGHT ENOUGH, SHE HASN'T EVEN HEARD ME.

THAT SLIPPER'S MINE. YOU'LL NEVER GET YOUR GREAT BIG PLATES O' MEAT IN IT!

FOR A MOMENT THERE, I THOUGHT IT WAS MISS B!

But all good things must come to an end . . .

THANKS A MILLION-SUE

GREAT! NOW TO GET ON WITH MY ESSAY!

And so, Monday morning . . .

COME OUT HERE, SUE STRONG! I WANT EVERYONE TO HEAR YOUR FASCINATING ESSAY — "THE PANTOMIME AS I SAW IT!"

THAT'S A BIT ROUGH ON SUE — BIGGER KNOWS SHE NEVER SAW IT!

WELL, I SAW CINDERELLA AS A PRETTY NICE GIRL — ONLY EVERYONE HAD IT IN FOR HER, 'COS SHE WAS SO SMALL! THEY GAVE HER ALL THE ROTTEN JOBS TO DO, AND MADE FUN OF HER SIZE, AND EVERYTHING.

THE UGLY SISTERS WERE THE WORST. OOOH, THEY WERE UGLY! AND SO SELFISH! Y'KNOW, THEY WERE THE KIND OF MISERABLE ROTTERS WHO'D WEAR A HAT, BIG AS A CARTWHEEL, TO THE THEATRE AN' REFUSE TO TAKE IT OFF.

WHAT? WHAT? WHAT? THIS ISN'T AN ESSAY!

I QUITE AGREE! IT'S A GRAND PIECE OF CREATIVE WRITING! AND AS SCHOOLS' INSPECTOR, I WANT TO CONGRATULATE YOU, MISS BIGGER, FOR ALLOWING SUCH TALENT TO FLOURISH IN YOUR CLASS!

OOOPS — I GOT A BIT CARRIED AWAY THERE! BUT LOOKS AS IF MY FAIRY GODMOTHER IS STILL KEEPING AN EYE ON ME, DOESN'T IT? ALL'S WELL THAT ENDS WELL!

STAR OF WONDER

THE three Campbell sisters—Jane, Julie and little Wendy—were fed up! It was Christmas Eve. The first Yuletide they'd spend in their new country home, and their father wouldn't be with them. The airline he worked for as a pilot was operating out of Amsterdam and he'd had to stay there for the Christmas flights.

"Nobody in the whole, wide world is as unlucky as we are," groaned Wendy, as the sisters trudged across the unfamiliar fields, bundles of picked holly in their arms. "I don't see why Dad can't be home for Christmas."

"You want everything!" replied Julie, the practical one. "Flying is dad's job—and he's earned enough to let us move to a lovely new country house, hasn't he? You just have to take the rough with the smooth."

An urgent whisper from Jane interrupted the bickering sisters. "Look . . . over there . . . gipsies!" She was pointing ahead to where, at the foot of a steep grassy slope dotted with sheep, stood a little wooden hut set on wheels.

Know-all Julie sniffed: "Gipsies? Huh! That's a shepherd's hut . . . and look—there's the shepherd himself."

Indeed, the door of the hut had just opened and, descending the wooden steps to the ground, was an elderly man wearing a rough jacket and gaiters. A black and white sheep dog trotted at his side. He waved a friendly walking stick at the sisters. "Collecting Christmas holly, eh? Well, come and say 'hello' . . . you're strangers to me—and I like to know everyone around these parts."

Soon, the girls were recounting their life story. How

24

they'd moved to the nearby village only a few weeks beforehand and that this would be their first Christmas there. "Well, you don't look very happy about it," smiled the shepherd. "Don't you like the Yuletide?"

"We love Christmas," piped little Wendy. "Only, our dad's a pilot and he'll be away for all of it!"

The shepherd regarded them gravely. "Dear me," he muttered. "That's sad, but if it's any consolation to you, I haven't spent Christmas with my family for years. You see, the first of the new lambs are due any time now . . . so I always pass the festive season here—alone in my little hut!"

A shocked Jane Campbell spoke first. "Oh, that's awful . . . aren't you lonely?"

"Lonely?" The shepherd forced a laugh. "Not with all these white-fleeced friends for company." He waved an arm at the flocks of sheep that grazed in the late-afternoon sun. "Still," he continued. "I do like company. Fancy a cuppa' tea, inside?"

The girls would! They'd been itching to see the inside of that cosy-looking hut. However, it wasn't at all as they'd imagined. The interior was cold, draughty. Bare wooden walls and ceiling. A single, rough bed, a cracked oil lamp and a tiny, smokey fire that spluttered beneath the heavy metal tea pot—that was it! They realised how lucky they were to be able to pass Christmas in a warm, decorated house!

The old man seemed to read their thoughts. "Not very Christmassy, is it? But then it hardly seems worthwhile decorating the hut just for me and Rex here." He patted his dog. "Besides, watching the flocks takes up all my time."

A little later, three chastened sisters were on their way home. Julie was the first to speak. "We thought we were unlucky, but at least we'll have company. Fancy him spending

Christmas Day staring at those blank wooden walls."

"But it doesn't have to be that way," gasped Jane. "Look, I've a little pocket money left . . . and the market will still be open. Come on!"

An hour later, they were on their way back to the hut as dusk closed in. Julie was sceptical. "One tatty Christmas tree—the last one—plus some left-over decorations. Doesn't seem much cheer here."

"But better than nothing," insisted Jane, as they reached the hut. "Knock on the door, Wendy."

No answer. "Probably out doing a final round of his sheep before dark," remarked Jane. "Even better. We can go in—and surprise him!"

Inside, the girls set to work. In no time the hut was transformed. Paper chains looped from the grimy walls to soot-blackened ceiling, balloons hung from the single roof support beam . . . and pride of place went to the rather sparse Christmas tree that, glistening with tinsel and topped with one of Wendy's miniature dolls wrapped in lace, graced an old flower pot.

"What the dickens . . . ?" It was the shepherd in the doorway . . . gasping his disbelief at the cheery scene.

"Surprise! Surprise!" chanted Wendy. "We didn't think it fair you should go without some Christmas cheer!"

"I-I don't know how to thank you," he began.

"Just seeing your face is thanks enough," smiled Jane. "Come on, you two, it's dark out . . . we'd better be getting back. Merry Christmas, sir." With that, the three sisters scampered down the wooden steps . . . into the dark December night.

"You can really see the stars out here in the country," breathed Julie, looking up at the spangled, night-frosted sky. "It must have been on just such a night that the Star of Wonder led the three wise men to the baby Jesus . . . on that first-

ever Christmas."

Wendy, who had been listening, was now staring over Julie's shoulder with ever-widening eyes. Suddenly, she let out a shriek. "Look. There's another Star of Wonder . . . big and bright, and it's just appeared. There it goes, moving over the hill! Quick . . . follow that star!" And next moment, she was haring past the hut and up the grassy night-shrouded hillside.

Her two sisters looked, and there—sure enough—was a bright, white light, blinking on and off as it moved slowly behind the hill. "Little fool," sniggered Julie the know-all. "That isn't a star . . . "

"Try telling Wendy the dreamer that," replied Jane. "We'd better run and catch up with her before she chases that 'star' all the way to the airfield!" So saying, they took to their heels in the wake of their excited little sister.

They caught her up at the very top of the hill. Julie, contemptuous, said: "Little idiot! Fancy thinking that was the Star of Wonder! It . . . "

"Be quiet," hissed Jane! "Can't you hear that . . . ?"

They could. Coming from a ring of trees a little way down the far side of the slope, was a faint, terrified bleating! As the girls rushed down the slope, the moon emerged from behind a small passing cloud—to reveal . . . a small pond, covered in thin ice, broken only near the bank. And in the water . . . a tiny, furry form . . . struggling, calling plaintively as it clawed at the frozen bank!

"Hold my hand . . . I'll lean out—try to grab it," commanded Jane. Next moment . . . "Gotcher!" She hauled the sodden white bundle ashore. "Come on . . . back to the hut . . . but fast!"

Soon, the old shepherd was warming the tiny, bleating huddle of life before the fire in his hut. "The first lamb of the season," he murmured. "Must have strayed from its mother

25

and tumbled into the pond. But for you, it would have drowned or frozen to death in minutes!"

"How horrible . . . at Christmas-time, too," breathed Wendy. "Lucky I followed that star. It led me right to the lamb!"

Gradually, the tiny creature's bleatings calmed and soon he was gulping milk from a bottle held by each of the sisters in turn. "He'll be all right now," whispered the shepherd. "But it's you three he has to thank for his life." Within an hour, the replete lamb was sleeping soundly, and only then did the sisters take their leave of the old shepherd.

Walking up towards the front door of their house some minutes later, the Campbell girls were surprised to see the door open and all the lights ablaze. And why was their mother standing in the hallway . . . face aglow with happiness? They soon found out!

"Ho, ho, ho! And where have you young wanderers been?" boomed a deep voice from the front room as they entered the house.

"Dad!" squeaked Wendy . . . "Dad!" shrilled Julie . . . "Dad?" gasped Jane. "B-but why aren't you . . ?"

"In Amsterdam?" her father smiled. "The plane I was to fly developed engine trouble and it's been grounded for a week. I managed to get a lift back in a light aircraft. It landed me at that small private airfield up the road . . . an hour ago or thereabouts!"

Julie was staring. "An hour ago! The 'star' Wendy saw. We knew it was the landing light of a small plane. It must have been *you* up there . . . coming home to us."

"No, it wasn't," jabbered angry Wendy. "It *was* the Star of Wonder. It led us to the baby lamb that was drowning . . . and then we rescued it . . . and took it back to the shepherd . . . and . . ."

"Hey, wait a minute," laughed their father. "One at a

time! What's this big adventure I've missed?" So, in fits and starts, the girls told him all about the lost lamb they'd saved and about the lonely Christmas vigil of the shepherd that they'd tried to make more cheery.

When they'd finished, Mr. Campbell scratched his chin thoughtfully. "Well, you've started the kind work. It's up to us to finish it!" he said.

And so it came to pass that while the Campbells were tucking into the best and happiest ever Christmas lunch, the next

day, the old shepherd in his hut was likewise feasting on a hot plate of roast turkey and all the trimmings, carried to him earlier on a covered dish by Jane, Julie and Wendy . . . compliments of Mr and Mrs Campbell.

Only one thing remained unsettled, however. Try as they might, no one . . . but no one . . . could ever convince Wendy that the Star of Wonder she followed to rescue the baby lamb had been nothing more than the winking landing lights of a small plane!

ANIMAL MAGIC

Please DO NOT PICNIC ON THE LAWN

BESSIE BUNTER

The Tammy A-Z of Sweet Dreams.

HAVE you ever had a dream come true? If so, then you foretold your own future, without knowing it at the time, and many powerful men in ancient times employed wise scholars to tell them what their dreams meant.

Much of the time, we dream about incidents that have happened to us during the day, or of a person we know well. And, if you think you don't dream, think again! We ALL dream, but some are more aware of it than others. Usually, a dream is best remembered because it has been rudely interrupted when the dreamer has woken suddenly. But, how often have you heard someone say: "I had a peculiar dream last night—couldn't make head nor tail of it!"

If YOU have said something like that, then see if your strange dream is listed here—and find out what it means!

ACCIDENTS in dreams are warnings that you need to be a little more careful, especially when it comes to friendships, and dealing with other people. To dream of an accident in a strange place means a slight set-back in romance. And to dream of ANGER or ARGUMENTS means the opposite to what you might think—that you are really fond of the people you are quarrelling with in your dreams, and they think a lot of you in return!

BREAD: to see yourself eating bread in a dream is a sign of happiness and good health to come. And it is also very lucky to see a BAKER at work in a dream—although it's not so lucky to dream of baking bread yourself. But, to dream of baking cakes and pies foretells many new and lasting friendships on the horizon.

CATS in a dream usually means that you are too trusting of a particular person. CATERPILLARS and CREEPY-CRAWLIES mean much the same thing in dreams—and there is also the old country rhyme about dreaming of CANDLES:

"A light that burns both bright and clear
Denotes some pleasant letter near.
But if dull the candle grows
It certain disappointment shows."

D is for DANCING—a very good omen in dreams. It's a sign of a gift of money and success for a future plan which you have in mind. And if you see the person with whom you are dancing in your dream, then there's good luck in store for him or her, too!

ELEPHANTS in dreams are extremely lucky symbols. They foretell some sort of inheritance, help from your friends, and marriage to a rich husband! Seeing EGGS in your dream also indicates some improvement in your future wealth, although, if any one of the eggs is cracked or broken, this could mean that you will lose something you value.

FLOATING AND FLYING. These are both very common dreams, and are thought to mean that the dreamer dreams through the day, as well as the night—in other words, living in a world of her own! To see FRIENDS in a dream, without any words being spoken means that your help will soon be needed by them; but if a friend calls your name, you will know that this is someone who thinks a great deal of you.

GALLOPING on a horse across open countryside is a sign that you can look forward to success in a special venture before long. And to dream of being in a lovely GARDEN is also a very lucky dream, because it means a boost to your budget and your spending! But, if you see yourself accepting a GIFT from a particular person, this is a sign that this person is not to be entirely trusted.

HAPPINESS in a dream is not what it might seem . . . It's a sign that you should take extra care for a little while, because there may be some unexpected difficulties ahead. But, if you dream about your HOME, then there is great joy in store for you, for a long while to come.

ITCHING is another dream which is quite common—and it means that you are worrying unnecessarily about a number of things. To see INSECTS in dreams indicates quite a few delays and set-backs in store, which could cause you a number of disappointments.

JOURNEYS in dreams are always a sign that your life will soon be changed in some way, often denoting a new home. But, if you are travelling by car in your dream, you should take things at a steady pace when the change finally comes. And a sea journey of some kind is forecast if you dream of making a JUMPER.

KITTENS, KNITTING and KISSING in dreams are all extremely fortunate omens, and signs of new friends, entertainments and interests on the horizon. But, if you dream of kissing a stranger, this is a warning to take extra care against losing your property—at least for the time being.

LAUGHING in a dream is a very lucky sign—an indication of some good fortune in the very near future—and, if you wake yourself up laughing, so much the better! A dream of LATENESS and rushing around in a panic is lucky too,

signifying that you are admired and respected by those around you.

MAGIC dreams foretell changes for the better at a time when you least expect them. Dreaming of hearing MUSIC is equally fortunate, indicating success and happiness. And, the more pleasing to the ear the music is, the luckier you will be!

NIGHTMARES can be very frightening for the dreamer, but they are usually lucky, and have the opposite meaning to the one you would think of. For instance, to dream you are unhappy and crying foretells a very happy future, and to see yourself scared is a sign of true courage within. Dreaming of being frightened by a horribly ugly person or being is considered to be one of the most fortunate omens, because it means good luck and success in a difficult task coming your way . . . So it seems that the luckiest people are those who are scared to go to sleep because of their nasty nightmares!

OLD people in dreams are a sign that help will come your way through lasting friendships— although if old people in your dream are sad-looking, it could mean a slight health problem. ORANGES and the colour ORANGE in dreams denotes a very happy future, with many pleasures to enjoy—with ORANGE BLOSSOM indicating a very happy marriage in the family, or for yourself!

PARTY dreams can be fairly lucky. But if you dream of any upsets happening at a party, or see yourself leaving before the end, it could mean that you may overlook a coming opportunity. To dream of carrying a PACKAGE in a dream indicates a disappointment coming your way—although PARCELS in dreams usually foretell changes about to take place, most of them for the better.

QUEENS in dreams are always very lucky—and to dream of any royalty is always the sign of unexpected good luck coming your way. It also means that you will receive all the help and assistance you need in achieving a special ambition.

R is for RAINBOW—one of the best dream indications of changes about to take place around you. But RAIN in a dream usually foretells some disappointing news, especially if you also see yourself plodding through a downpour—but the lighter the rain, the slighter your coming difficulties. And to dream of RUNNING in a dream is another omen of set-backs and disappointments. However, these will not be serious, and you should overcome them quite easily!

SADNESS in dreams is not a sign of misery and bad luck—quite the opposite! In fact, this dream always signifies that you will soon be able to stop worrying about a particular matter, and that great happiness is in store—and much the same meaning also applies if you dream that you are SIGHING. On the other hand, if you dream that you are SINGING happily, this indicates that there will be quite a few difficulties for you to overcome in the future.

The Tammy A-Z of Sweet Dreams...

TOMBSTONES and cemeteries may seem grim and morbid, but it's surprising how often they crop up in our dreams! To see yourself wandering among tombstones and reading the inscriptions foretells a long life; and, if you see yourself with a friend in the dream, this indicates lots of friends throughout your life, and much to look forward to in the future. It's also the sign of a very happy marriage!

UNKNOWN PEOPLE in your dream is the sign of a lot of travel in the near future—and the happier the people look, the better the trip will be. And any kind of UNHAPPINESS in dreams is very lucky for the dreamer, because it foretells good fortune for some time to come, as well as being an indication that you will tackle a difficult problem wisely.

VOICES in dreams are a sign of gossip which should not be listened to by the dreamer, because there is usually someone in the background who is trying to stir up trouble. This type of dream also indicates a few hold-ups and delays in a special project.

WRITING in the course of a dream is a sign that you will receive a letter from a friend you'd almost forgotten about, possibly from abroad. And if you see yourself writing in a hurry, you will be asking someone for advice very shortly. For a dream of WATER, we have another interesting old verse—

"Waterfalls mean troubles and strife,
But where flowing smoothly, so flows your life;
When water looks thick, troubles are near,
But most happy you, when 'tis seen to look clear."

X-RAY pictures in a dream have a fairly obvious interpretation—it simply means that you can expect some form of medical examination in the near future.

YULE-LOGS blazing in a hearth are one of the luckiest things to dream about! It indicates lots of prosperity and freedom from want in the future. But seeing YELLOW in a dream is nearly always the sign of jealousy towards you, particularly yellow flowers.

ZODIAC signs are very fortunate symbols when you see any of them in a dream, because they signify that you will benefit greatly from study and learning.

33

34

35

LIKE TO WISH YE A HAPPY STAY... BUT THE LAIRD'S BEEN A HARD TASK-MASTER EVER SINCE HE INHERITED GROMMACH CASTLE!

A CHRISTMAS BONUS, GILLIE? TO FRITTER ON PRESENTS FOR THE CHILDREN? NAE CHANCE... BACK TAE WORK!

WEEL, WEEL... DON'T STAND THERE IDLE AS STATUES... THERE'S WORK TO BE DONE, TENDEN' THE LIVESTOCK. OOTSIDE, THE PAIR O' YE!

HUH! THIS BLOKE MAKES SCROOGE LOOK LIKE A DUTCH UNCLE. AND NOW THEIR MONEY-MAKING SCHEME'S FALLEN THROUGH, DON'T RECKON JED AND GERT WILL BE BACK TO BAIL ME OUT IN A HURRY!

Outside, Bella found an early chance to lighten her spirits...

GOT TO FEED THIS LOT AND... HEY, BELLA... WHIT ARE YE DOIN'?

WATCH AND YOU'LL SEE... CAN'T KEEP A GOOD GYMNAST DOWN, I ALWAYS SAY!

HEY, TERRIFIC... YOU MEAN THAT ABOUT BEIN' A GYMNAST?

YEP... MIND YOU, THE VAULT AIN'T MY STRONGEST POINT, AN' IT'S AS TRICKY ON A BULL AS ON A "HORSE", YOU TRY IT!

EASY AND... OOOH!

LOOK OUT... YOU'VE MISSED WITH THE LEFT HAND!

OOH... MY ARM!

CRIKEY, SHE'S HURT HERSELF... AND IT'S ALL MY FAULT FOR LETTING AN UNTRAINED GIRL HAVE A BASH!

The Laird of Grommach was far from pleased...

A SLIGHT SPRAIN... BUT THAT'LL MEAN A CUT IN THE WORK SHE CAN DO... ALL BECAUSE O' YE DAFT SKYLARKING. WEEL, YOU CAN DO HER SHARE O' THE CHORES FROM NOW ON... AND YE CAN CUT THE GYMNASTICS RIGHT OOT, YE HEAR?

I HEAR... BUT THAT'S EASIER SAID THAN DONE!

37

THOUGHT YOU'D BE DOWN HERE. BETTER GET BACK TAE THE CASTLE. . . OLD MISERY'S MOANING FAE HIS SUPPER!

SORRY, KIDS. . . DUTY CALLS!

I WISH DAD WERE MORE INTERESTED IN GYMNASTICS. MIGHT TAKE HIS MIND OFF HIS TROUBLES. THANKS TO THE LAIRD, IT'LL BE A LEAN CHRISTMAS FOR US!

YEAH. . . CHRISTMAS! SEASON OF GOODWILL. . . EXCEPT HERE. SOMETHING'S GOTTA BE DONE ABOUT THAT!

A chance came on Christmas Eve. . .

LOOK, BEFORE YE TURN IN, WILL YE CLEAR THIS RUBBISH OOTSIDE SOMEWHERE? IT'S LEFT OVER FROM MY NIECE'S FAMILY'S LAST VISIT. AH CAN'T ABIDE CLUTTER. . . OR BRIGHT COLOURS!

NOT SURPRISED! RECKON THIS CASTLE COULD BE RENAMED "GLOOMY VIEW". STILL, THOSE TOYS LOOK GOOD AS NEW. . . AND THEM LONG, RED CURTAINS . . . I WONDER. . ?

When the rest of the castle slept, something stirred. . .

AS I HOPED, WASN'T ANY TROUBLE FINDING SHEEP'S WOOL CAUGHT ON THE FIELD WIRES. NOW, WITH A BIT OF LUCK — AND THE LOAN OF A SEWING MACHINE — I RECKON I CAN "RECYCLE" THE LAIRD'S "RUBBISH!"

And later, as a snow-tinged dawn broke above the Gillie's cottage. . .

WON'T WIN NO AWARD FOR DRESS DESIGNING. . . BUT "SANTA" BARLOW'S COME TO CALL!

HUH? SOMETHING TAPPING OOTSIDE!

AHA. . . THANKS FOR OPENING THE WINDOW. . . DON'T RECKON I COULD HAVE MADE IT DOWN THE CHIMNEY!

AH—AH DINNA BELIEVE IT . . .

WOTCHER! I MEAN. . . HO, HO, HO. . . HAPPY CHRISTMAS, KIDS!

OOH. . . SANTA. . . HE'S COME, AFTER ALL!

BLESS YOU, BELLA!

38

Her good deed done, tired and weary, Bella trailed back to the castle . . .

MY OLD LIFE SEEMS A WORLD AWAY. WISH I WERE AT WEMBLEY NOW . . . DOIN' MY FAVOURITE BEAM ROUTINE . . .

THAT GAVE ME A RIGHT WARM FEELING! JUST AS WELL, TOO . . . IT'S SO COLD AND GLOOMY HERE . . . YAAAAAAWW! HARDLY SEEMS WORTH GOIN' TO BED!

FORWARD WALKOVER . . DISMOUNT . . .

BELLA . . . LOOK OUT!

WHAT . . . UUUH . . . NO . . . I'M FALLING . . . FALLING!

OOH, MUST HAVE SLEEPWALKED ON THE BANISTERS . . . DREAMIN' I WAS ON THE BEAM!

WHAT'S ALL THE ? . . . AAAAAAGH! NO . . !

THAT — THAT WAS CENTURIES OLD . . . JACOBEAN! OCH, YOU'LL BE WORKING HERE FOR MONTHS TO PAY FOR THAT!

HUH . . . JUST AS WELL IT WEREN'T A NEW ONE, THEN . . . BUT WHAT'S THIS OLD ROLL OF PAPER I FOUND?

A miraculous change came over the ferocious Laird of Grommach . . .

WHAT IS IT THEN ? WHAT'S CRACKED THAT SMILE INTO YOUR FACE . . ?

THESE — THE TITLES AND DEEDS TO THE ESTATE OF GROMMACH. MY HALF-BROTHER LEFT ALL THIS TO ME, BUT AFTER HIS DEATH, THE DOCUMENTS WENT MISSING. I'VE BEEN ON TENTERHOOKS FOR MONTHS, NOT KNOWING WHETHER I MIGHT LOSE THE ESTATE!

SO IT WAS THE WORRY THAT MADE YOU SUCH AN OLD GROUCH!

AYE... BUT NOW I'M A NEW AND CAREFREE MAN. BELLA, THE DEBT IS SETTLED... YE'VE GIVEN ME THE FINEST CHRISTMAS PRESENT EVER. WHO COULD WISH FOR MORE?

YOUR GILLIE'S FAMILY, FOR A START. HOW ABOUT SPREADING SOME CHEER THEIR WAY?

YE'RE RIGHT. I'LL GO... RIGHT NOW!

NOW I BELIEVE IN MIRACLES. LOOKS LIKE CHRISTMAS IS GOIN' TO BE SOMETHING, AFTER ALL. BUT WHAT'S THE BETTING JED AND GERT TURN UP TO SHARE IT?

Bella needn't have worried, for, at that moment...

GURR! MILES FROM ANYWHERE WITH A PUNCTURE AND AN EMPTY TANK! WHAT A START TO CHRISTMAS DAY!

NEVER MIND, JED. WE GOT THIS CHICKEN WE "FOUND" FOR DINNER — AND WE AIN'T WORKING OUR HIDES OFF FOR NO LAIRD, ARE WE? WE'RE IN CLOVER, COMPARED TO BELLA!

But, many miles away...

EAT, DRINK AND BE MERRY, ONE AND ALL. THERE'LL BE CELEBRATIONS ALL THE WAY TO HOGMANAY!

EVERYTHING'S TURNED OUT SO WELL, I COULD JUMP FOR JOY — AND WHY NOT?

TRUST BELLA... A DISPLAY OF HIGHLAND DANCING — GYMNASTICS STYLE!

NEVER KNEW WHETHER I WAS ON MY HEAD OR ME HEELS THIS CHRISTMAS... BUT ALL'S WELL THAT ENDS WELL, EH?

FUN ALL THE WAY TO HOGMANAY, THE LAIRD SAID. AND JUST FER ONCE, JED AND GERT HAVEN'T MUSCLED-IN ON MY GOOD FORTUNE! SERVES 'EM RIGHT!

The End

40

ANIMAL MAGIC

W HAT would YOU like to see in TAMMY? Sports features? Beauty advice? More puzzles and things to do? Well, now's your chance to put some of those ideas into practice, and —

Join the

All you have to do is imagine yourself in the TAMMY office for just one day . . .

1) The day begins with a pile of readers' letters on the Editor's desk, all asking for something new and exciting in the paper. What would you suggest —
a) *a new type of serial?*
b) *more colour pages?*
c) *a regular TAMMY cartoon?*
d) *a weekly pop music and T.V. review?*

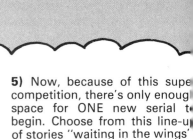

2) The TAMMY team decide to give the readers some sort of special treat. Would this be —
a) *samples of beauty products?*
b) *a voucher for a free chocolate bar or packet of crisps?*
c) *free tickets for a show in your area?*
d) *a free badge or brooch, stuck on the front cover?*

4) It's a competition that's being discussed now — and you're being asked for your suggestions on prizes which girls would like to win. Would you put forward:

a) *lunch or dinner with a famous personality?*
b) *a luxury weekend stay in a big city?*
c) *a cine outfit?*
d) *a portable television?*

5) Now, because of this supe competition, there's only enoug space for ONE new serial t begin. Choose from this line-u of stories "waiting in the wings"

a) *"All Alone Alice" — about girl caring alone for her family;*
b) *"Sally's Starry Trail" – th story of a girl in charge of space–ship;*
c) *"Desert Island Diana";*
d) *"Tina's Team", about a du sports team competing for trophy.*

3) And when it comes to something for an eye-catching, attractive cover, what would you like to see?
a) *a funny cartoon;*
b) *a party scene;*
c) *a comic strip story;*
d) *a picture of animals.*

Tammy and MISTY

Team!

1st PRIZE

6) Each page in TAMMY is set out on a large "story-board" — and one gets LOST just before everything is due to go to the printer! How would you fill the gap?
a) put in a page of puzzles and jokes?
b) print photographs of animals or someone famous?
c) reprint a feature like a "Hobby-Horse" article or "Tuck-in with Tammy" cookery page?
d) publish some more readers' letters?

7) Suppose you were the EDITOR, and you received lots of requests for the weekly horoscope to be extended from a half-page to a page. Would you —
a) make plans for a full page at the start of each month?
b) put in little "Did You Know?" pieces about the zodiac, dotted throughout the mag?
c) keep things as they are, but put in extra horoscope info. when the space is available?
d) want to try it for a few weeks to see how it goes?

8) Time comes to start planning the TAMMY Annual, and you have to decide what the main aim should be —
a) a good read from cover to cover;
b) value for money;
c) a book which any girl would love as a present;
d) something which girls will want to "dip into" again and again.

9) If you were asked to think of an entirely new page feature, what would be your first suggestion —
a) television and film gossip?
b) beauty hints and news?
c) craft and how-to-make?
d) features on pop stars?

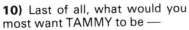

10) Last of all, what would you most want TAMMY to be —
a) *entertaining?*
b) *something to look forward to each week?*
c) *an interesting paper to read?*
d) *a mag that's well worth the money?*

NOW CHECK YOUR SCORE —

Question 1	a=4;	b=3;	c=2;	d=1;
Question 2	a=3;	b=2;	c=1;	d=4;
Question 3	a=2;	b=1;	c=4;	d=3;
Question 4	a=1;	b=4;	c=3;	d=2;
Question 5	a=4;	b=3;	c=2;	d=1;
Question 6	a=3;	b=2;	c=1;	d=4;
Question 7	a=2;	b=1;	c=4;	d=3;
Question 8	a=1;	b=4;	c=3;	d=2;
Question 9	a=4;	b=3;	c=2;	d=1;
Question 10	a=3;	b=2;	c=1;	d=4;

For a score between 32–40 points — it's the TAMMY EDITOR's job to plan the paper from week to week, to decide which serials and stories are to be included, and which new features should be introduced — and your strong-minded and clear-thinking judgement could give you a flying start as an assistant! You have the ability to be an excellent planner and to decide exactly which goal you should be aiming for — and you can probably turn on the charm to persuade other people to do what you think is best . . . something all editors learn to do! You have very definite ideas and opinions of your own, but you also enjoy learning about new subjects to keep your lively mind fully occupied. You are likely to be very good at handling a budget, too!

Score 27–31 points — and you could be just the person to help our ART EDITOR! Your good imagination and flair for design would be great when it comes to choosing illustrations for features and working out how the pictures in a serial would appear. (People like those in the TAMMY TEAM call this "visualising".) The ART EDITOR also has to meet all different types of artists and see how their work and artistic style can best be used in the paper — something which requires the qualities of good taste and a keen sense of artistic arrangement which you appear to have, and you are also likely to have a knack of dealing with different people. Our ART EDITOR could probably have made a very good Interior Designer or Landscape Gardener as well!

Score between 21 and 26 points — we'd think of introducing you to our ART ASSISTANT, whose job it is to design the title-headings, make any alterations in art-work, and set out illustrations and drawings ready for printing. It's work which requires a lot of patience to get the best possible result — and your quiet, painstaking approach to almost everything you do would definitely be a plus in your favour! Like TAMMY'S ART ASSISTANT, you are also likely to have the gift of using your hands equally well as your brain, and you cannot bear to rush at something, or to leave a job half-finished — you are too much of a perfectionist for that! You are probably quite a critical person, too — someone who is always looking for ways to improve things. And, in the end, you usually do!

For a score of 20 and under — you could be stepping into the shoes of the TAMMY SUB EDITOR one day! Your eye for detail would soon spot any mistakes in the "copy" (that's what the TAMMY TEAM call words for a feature or a picture story), and your thoughtfulness and consideration of other people's views and opinions would be much appreciated when it comes to helping a team to work smoothly together. You also seem to be the type who can be trusted to work alone, without being easily distracted or flustered — very useful when it comes to "editing" or cutting down words to fit into balloon spaces! And, because he or she has to work with all the members of an Editorial Team, a SUB EDITOR has to adapt to lots of different ideas and tricky situations which may occur — something which would certainly stimulate the mind of an "I'll-try-anything-once" girl like you!

Tammy and MISTY PUZZLES

NAMES AND ADDRESSES:
Can you discover the names and addresses of the two girls hidden in these sketches?

ANSWER:
Dora White, 15, Belford Crescent, Glasgow. Fiona Mackey, 28, Manor Way, Weymouth.

OPPOSITES:
Six of these words in picture form are the opposite in meaning to six of the others. Solve the clues then pick the pairs!

ANSWER:
Above — below; Short — long; Win — lose; Joy — sorrow; True — false; Right — wrong.

FOUR WAYS:
These letters will make four different words. What are they?

ANSWER:
Mean, mane, name, amen.

FURNITURE PROBLEM:
Six pieces of furniture are shown on this house. Put the word-pieces together correctly to see what they are.

ANSWER:
Stool, cabinet, settee, desk, table, chair.

CAREER:
Rearrange the initial letters of these objects to name someone who takes care of business affairs.

ANSWER:
Secretary.

WORD PUZZLE:
Can you put the same word (a measure of length) in front of all these picture words to make six new words?

ANSWER:
Football, foothills, footmark, foot-lights, footstool.
Footbridge,

COLLECTORS' CORNER

EVER thought about making an Antiques Collection of your own? Probably not. Yet it's something which could lead you to lots of interesting places, help you make new friends, and give you a lifetime of pleasure.

Many of us think of collectors being rich people who can afford to splash out thousands of pounds on just one item. But there are lots of things which can be bought very cheaply, either in small "junk" shops, market stalls, and even jumble sales.

Whatever your particular interests are, there's a wide choice for bargain-price collectors, and the list of collectors' items is increasing all the time. Only a few years ago, nobody gave much thought to the household containers which Victorians had to use before tin-cans and throwaway packs came on the scene. But nowadays, stone jars and bottles are very much sought-after by collectors.

And it isn't only really old stuff that's being collected, either. Your Dad's wooden-cased wireless set may not look much, but if it's in working order, there are an increasing number of amateur collectors who would be interested in it.

Mugs and china plates made in the 1950s might also be quite valuable if they commemorated a special event, or advertised a commercial product, such as meat-cubes or drinking chocolate — to say nothing of all those little

Items made in brass have been very popular among collectors for a long time.

Both the boot and "Mr. Punch" shown here were made around 1870 to hold matches, before safety matches were carried around in cardboard or splinter-wood match-boxes.

The little brass candlesticks are a little older, dating from around 1850.

Here's another up-and-coming collector's item — and it's not part of a dolls' tea-set, as you might think! These were tradesmen's samples, which salesmen carried around in suitcases to get orders. Samples were made miniature-size so that, although buyers could see the pattern and style of the full-size tea-set, the salesman could get more samples into his case to give a larger choice, and carry them around more easily.

Nursery rhymes were always very popular in designs, because nearly everybody knew them. These samples illustrate "Where Are You Going To, My Pretty Maid?" and were made in the Liverpool Road Pottery, North London, about 1900.

There were a good many of these miniature trademen's samples made for all sorts of other things, too — especially those items which were too big, bulky or fragile for the salesmen to carry around easily. Things like pieces of furniture, clocks, carpets — even fireplaces! Most of them are quite easily identified by the maker's name and trade mark somewhere on the item — so just see if you can find any!

crocheted mats and doilies which Grandma's probably got tucked away at the back of a drawer. Hand-crocheted items of this sort are becoming the "in-things" to be collected — so have a hunt through the White Elephant stall at the next jumble sale, and see what you can find!

Old clothes are fast becoming big business, as well, particularly garments from the 1930s and 1940s, when fewer clothes were being made because of shortages caused by the Second World War.

Talking of the last War, tell Granddad not to bung his old uniform or bits of service equipment into the dustbin just yet. Regimental buttons, belt-buckles, water-bottles, ammunition pouches, holster cases and cap badges are very high in the popularity stakes where collectors are concerned.

Not sure about what sort of things you'd like to collect? Then it's a good idea to think about the things you enjoy doing, and the subjects which interest you. If you're keen on art and design, you might consider making a collection of miniature paintings, greetings cards, post-cards or old photographs — plenty to choose from at rock-bottom prices if you

look around!

Dolls are becoming more expensive collectors' items, but there are often the more modern celluloid, rag or wooden dolls for sale, which you may like to dress in your own fashion creations.

Cookery enthusiasts can usually discover old cookery books fairly easily, as well as items of cutlery and cooking equipment used in the days before electric mixers and labour-saving devices. It already seems that household equipment will be a very popular subject for collectors within a few years — so best start your collection without delay!

Don't reject pieces which have slight flaws, like chips, discolourations or dents. Not only will they be a lot cheaper to buy, but you can learn just as much from a slightly damaged item as you can from something in mint condition. And most amateur collectors agree, there's something very pleasing in looking after an object which has been loved and cherished for a long time, in spite of its less-than-perfect condition.

Items in precious or semi-precious metals which have the original owner's initials engraved, or an inscription, are not nearly so

expensive as unmarked pieces, either. Of course, an engraved item will not increase in value so much as other collectors' pieces, but it will always keep the market value of the actual metal used — so you won't lose money by buying a marked item, and it is one of the few ways in which an amateur collector can obtain a similar piece to one owned by a more wealthy customer.

As your collection progresses, you will find yourself gradually becoming quite a detective, too — tracing little clues from the things you buy which will help you to find out how old they are, and where they were made. Local museums are always very helpful in putting young collectors on the right track.

Collectors usually become so enthusiastic about their collection that they often decide to specialise in one particular aspect of it, mostly to prevent themselves wanting to buy everything they see!

But whatever you decide about your own collection, all of us at "TAMMY" would like to wish you — Happy Hunting!

(And may everything you want be "just the right price!")

A Tammy treat every week of the year

Tammy doesn't have to be just an annual treat — you can enjoy all your favourites every week in Tammy and Misty weekly paper! Keep in touch with Bella's adventures, the Storyteller's mysteries, the life of servant-girl Molly Mills and many more gripping stories! There's fun, too, with Wee Sue, Bessie Bunter and Edie PLUS features on pop, TV, fashion hints and advice, puzzles, jokes and your weekly horoscope!
Place a regular order with your newsagent today!

BESSIE BUNTER

...THROUGH ROSE-COLOURED GLASSES

THE school eye test had confirmed it. No two ways about it – I needed glasses. After years of tripping over kerbs and walking into lamp posts, it was either get specs or spend my life tending bumps and bruises!

Needless to say, I was anything but happy about it that morning before school when Mum and Dad led me towards Prices, the opticians, to choose the new glasses. You could say I was in a right old sulk – and you'd be right! Dad tried to cheer me up.

"Come on, now, Janet. Glasses aren't so bad, you can choose some quite fashionable tints and frames. It'll seem a whole new world once your eyesight's one hundred per cent."

He needn't have bothered. With a, "You choose the flaming things . . . I don't care!" I sulked outside the shop, while my parents went in. I'd never clapped short-sighted eyes on Mr Price the optician, but I could tell he was a cheery old soul by the peals of laughter and merry chatter that floated out from his shop.

Soon, Mum and Dad were back outside, holding out a spectacle case, smiling encouragingly. Before they could start drivelling about what a lucky girl I was, I'd snatched the offending article and stormed off through the grey city drizzle . . . towards school, in a right old mood!

Half a mile later, I'd calmed down sufficiently to risk a peek inside the spectacle case. And there they were . . . my new – and dreaded – glasses. Well, they didn't look so bad. Thin, stylish frames . . . the glass itself tinted a delicate shade of pink.

Taking a breath, I put them on for the first time. "What on earth . . ?" As if by magic, the winter drizzle had turned to a gentle spring shower. Colourful birds twittered in the trees. A whole new world unfolded, glowing a gentle shade of pink. My spirits sky-rocketed.

Not for long, though. There were the school gates. I'd have to face everyone . . . the inevitable jibes about my new specs . . . and on top of that, it was double maths after assembly! What a day! Next moment, I was shouldering my way through the crowd of class-mates in the playground, tensed – waiting for the comments, ready to hit out. There weren't any comments, though, just friendly, glowing faces, smiles, waves. I'd never noticed before what a happy-go-lucky bunch my school-mates were. This was certainly an eye-opener!

Then, coming towards me, a rose-coloured halo seeming to surround her, was the bane of my life – Diane Clemments. Diane always tried to pal-up with me, but she had more than her share of annoying habits, chewing the ends of her hair, sucking pencil tops, clicking her fingers incessantly, fidgetting. Funny, though, today she didn't seem annoying at all . . . quite the reverse.

Soon, Diane and I were side by side in class, chatting like the old friends we weren't, when a shadow fell across the desk. "Enjoying our little natter, are we? I'm sure we'd all like to hear just what has aroused your interest."

Miss Brewster, the maths teacher. As always, sour as a crab apple.

"Er, well . . ." I stammered, a wide grin almost splitting my face in two. "We were just remarking on the lovely new hair-do you have today. Really suits you, Miss."

We hadn't been of course, but it was true! I'd had to blink twice behind my new rose-tinged specs to be sure that the teacher taking the class really was Miss Brewster. Her mousey locks seemed to have been swept back into a stunning new style. Shows what can be done, with even the poorest materials!

I'd said the right thing. Miss Brewster flushed a deeper pink than she already appeared to my eyes. "Oh, really? You think so . . . you're not just making fun?" she simpered. Next moment, with an off-hand, "Er, revise, everyone. I shall have to go and . . . er . . . check something," she was out of the door.

"Off to the staff room for a preen in front of the mirror, I'll be bound," I remarked to Diane. Well, why not? It would do her good to feel special – for once.

Miss Brewster wasn't back for half an hour and then – what a change! Gone were the acid tones and sour expression. In their place, a kindly voice . . . a touch of sympathy when the class failed to make head or tail of her mathematical hieroglyphics. Somehow, she seemed to forget the double helping of homework she usually prescribed just to make our evenings complete. All in all . . . a great start to a great day!

And so it went on. School dinner almost edible and the other lessons seemed actually interesting for once. Of course, it helped that I didn't have to squint at the blackboard to see what was going on . . . though the pink tint that the whole world acquired did tend to be rather confusing. But the great thing was the other girls.

I'd always been a bit shy, stand-offish, even, with them . . . unsure of myself . . . or them. Today, though, it was a different world. By the time school was over, I'd found hidden depths in just about everyone – and more than a dozen kindred spirits. I found myself booked up for a couple of parties, shopping trips, visits, you name it! A fabulously busy week ahead!

Home and – yes – I even enjoyed helping Mum with the housework . . . now I didn't have to peer short-sightedly around to avoid coming a cropper over the coffee table and suchlike. What a cosy little nest our house was . . . never seen it like that before. Then sitting down, waiting for Dad to come

home, I heard it again . . . that sound that had been bothering me ever since I'd come in . . . that faint scratching at the door. Come to think of it, Mum was looking sheepish. I soon found out why!

"Er . . . Janet . . . I-I know you're not over-keen on dogs . . ." she began. Well, she was right there. I didn't mind dogs . . . in other people's lives, but in mine, no thank you very much! Soulful doggy eyes following you around the room, moulted hairs all over that new dress, the lovable – I don't think – puppy-dog habit of chewing up expensive shoes! Not my cup of tea at all!

Now, Mum had flushed pinker still before my rose-tinted sight, and then it came out, in a rush. "Well, there was this puppy down at the animal shelter. Going to be put down it was, and I couldn't resist it and it'll be ever so well behaved . . . and you'll get used to it, I know you will and . . ." It had happened – what I'd always dreaded – we'd acquired a canine home-wrecker!

Still, after a day like today, I just couldn't blow my top . . . not even if Mum had installed a sea lion in the bath that would need feeding every time anyone took a sploosh! I was in that good a mood. Then in he came . . . Mum's waif-hound . . . and my heart melted. Snow white hair, silky coat, warm brown eyes that peered adoringly up at me from a friendly, impish face. Mum was right . . . he was irresistible!

There was just one hurdle to overcome to round off that perfect day . . . the disco down at the town

hall. I was determined to go, and not shut myself away like a hermit. But I still felt rather self-conscious about my new, bespectacled image. Also, there was another fly in the ointment, in the rather distinctive, semi-human shape of Lawrence Cadwallader!

Now, everyone said he had a heart of gold and a sense of humour that would have made John Cleese seem as solemn as a judge. So far, so good. Trouble was . . . he also had a face like the back of a bus! Yes, Lawrence would be there, and – as always – he'd be pestering me to dance. I'd been pretty rude to him at the youth club "do" a fortnight before, but it hadn't put him off. His sister, Sandy, said he'd got a giant-sized crush on me . . . big deal!

However, specs or no specs . . . Lawrence Cadwallader or no Lawrence Cadwallader . . . I wasn't going to let anything spoil my perfect day. So, off to the disco I went . . . dolled up to the nines.

If I do say so myself, my new rose-coloured glasses did suit me and I'd got this fab new skirt and top. My hair hadn't done its usual trick of whipping into tightly coiled springs under the drier. In short, I didn't feel like a million dollars . . . but certainly five hundred thousand of them!

The disco! Coloured strobe lights on my pink specs certainly gave an odd but "fun" ef-fect . . . and the sounds the DJ was playing seemed better than any I'd heard before. That wasn't the main thing, though. The real clincher was this fantastic-looking fella asking if I fancied a dance. You bet I did!

Perhaps it was being short-sighted, but I hadn't noticed this boy at previous discos. He could dance well, too . . . something most of the other lads there couldn't do . . . and he was such fun to be with! A non-stop patter of jokes, comments, anecdotes . . . you name it, he had it! A really great guy!

That disco seemed never-ending. When I think back on it, I just picture me and this bloke (Larry, his name was . . . oddly familiar) dancing the night away like some latter-day Fred Astaire and Ginger Rogers. Fantastic. All things must end, though. Half-eleven . . . and I told Larry I'd better go before I turned into a pumpkin. My new friend replied that he'd be honoured to escort me safely to my door . . . so off we went together – happy!

Outside, a pink-tinged moon was shining as we ran, chasing and laughing through the back streets that led to my home. All at once, I felt I was walking on air, till a shouted warning and strong hands grabbing my shoulders, brought me back to reality. I'd stepped off the towpath in canal lane, and nearly finished the evening with the ducking of my life! Lucky I had Larry, my knight in shining armour, around to rescue me!

Soon, after saying a "Cheerio, see you tomorrow," to Larry (that name, still naggingly familiar), I was back in my room, sighing contentedly after the happiest day of my life. A day I'd dreaded when I first knew I'd have to wear specs!

Morning! I woke to the slop of rain against the window. "Still, never mind," I thought, reaching for the glasses, that I'd left on my bedside cabinet.

They weren't there! I dashed myopically – shortsightedly, that is – down the stairs . . . my head filled with questions. What had happened to the glasses? Had it all been a dream, or . . . "Woooaaaaah!" Crash! There, sitting on the bottom stair, just where I could – and had – tripped right over him, lay the ugliest, mangiest, hairiest, "lollopy-est" dog imaginable. I remember thinking that mutt just couldn't have been the lovable puppy Mum had introduced me to the day before!

Before I could say anything however, the front room door opened and looking down at me were Mum, Dad – and a gent I'd never seen before. He looked happy, relieved . . . and he was wearing my new rose-coloured glasses! Mum answered my unasked question, "This is Mr. Price, the optician. Apparently, at the shop yesterday, we picked up *his* glasses instead of your new ones, by mistake. He came round this morning as soon as he'd worked out what must have happened!"

"I couldn't manage without my glasses," smiled Mr. Price. "Nothing seemed quite the same." I could well believe that!

Soon, the be-spectacled optician had left, beaming happily, leaving me looking a little forlornly at the fashionable brown-framed glasses that were *really* mine. Shame. I'd got quite attached to those pink-tinted goggles that had come into my life the day before. But still, I couldn't be upset about anything . . . not even that strange, hairy – and dangerous – creature I'd come a cropper over in the hall!

"Er, Janet . . ." began Mum, breaking into my thoughts, "'Boofuls' – our puppy – well . . . he . . . er . . . found one of your new suede boots and . . . er . . ."

"Chewed it up!" I howled in horror. The destructive Boofuls had just appeared in the doorway, the remains of what had once been a fashionable – and expensive – suede boot, dangling from his jaws. "I knew it! That's what comes of . . ."

In mid-sentence, I stopped. Did it really matter all that much? Did I really want to blow my top as I would have done before I'd got those rose-coloured glasses? No. Patting Boofuls firmly on his moulting head, I left for school, my real glasses firmly in place. Outside, the winter drizzle had returned, but I didn't mind.

At school, there was Diane, chewing her hair and clicking her fingers, as infuriatingly as ever . . . but we'd become friends, so why spoil it? We'd discovered we had lots of things in common, after all. Maths . . . and Miss Brewster . . . her hair-do not quite the creation I thought I'd seen the day before – but did it matter? She was still as nice as pie. School dinners? Well . . . you can't expect something edible two days running, can you?

The greatest shock was still to come. Home time . . . and there, waiting outside the school gates, looking like a stand-in for Frankenstein's monster, was that walking facial disaster I'd been avoiding like the plague for weeks – Lawrence Cadwallader. What did he want? Why was he smiling at me, like someone who's just seen a long lost – and very rich – uncle? I soon found out.

"Hello, luv," he grinned. "Well, here I am."

"I can see that," said I, cold as school custard. "And what do you want, Lawrence?" He stiffened a bit, surprised. "Lawrence? It was Larry at the disco yesterday . . . and how come the cold shoulder? I thought we'd really clicked!"

Then it hit me! Larry, the name had seemed so familiar . . . because it *was* Lawrence . . . Lawrence Cadwallader, who'd swept me off my feet at the disco. How could that be? Not even in the kindest light, could Lawrence be described as handsome.

My brain whirled. First the puppy, then Diane, Miss Brewster and now Lawrence . . . all so different from how they'd appeared the day before, when I'd seen them all through my new rose-coloured glasses!

That was it! Suddenly, I knew that was exactly what I had done! My new rose-coloured glasses had shown everyone and everything in a new – and better – light!

Incredible, but now I know why the optician always looks so cheerful these days. As for me, well, I never did view the world through my own glasses, the way I'd seen it through the rose-coloured ones. But, thanks to them, I've become a confirmed dog lover, I've a super new round of school friends, an understanding teacher and – last but not least – the wittiest, cleverest boyfriend imaginable!

I'd never swop Larry now . . . even though, just sometimes, I wish he'd turn up for a date with a box over his head! But you can't have everything in life, and I've got a lot going for me now!

And whenever I feel down in the dumps, I take time out to think back . . . and remember what my world looked like, viewed through those rose-coloured glasses!

ANIMAL MAGIC

BACKHAND BILLIE

The Rosewell Academy, where the cream of Britain's young female tennis players are provided with every facility to develop their skills . . .

AN ACE! TERRIFIC SERVING.

GOOD GAME, ANTHEA. YOU'RE REALLY PUTTING YOUR STROKES TOGETHER WELL!

THANKS, JILL. THE COACHING AT THE ACADEMY HAS HELPED US ALL.

The girls' peace was suddenly shattered —

CALL THAT LAWN TENNIS? MORE LIKE YAWN TENNIS, YOU BORING BUNCH OF DUFFERS!

WHAT THE — ?

YOU'RE TRESPASSING, YOU CHEEKY WRETCH! GET OUT OF HERE BEFORE I CALL THE POLICE!

OH YEAH? DO THAT AN' YOU'LL END UP WITH EGG ON YOUR FACE!

CALM DOWN, JILL, IT WAS JUST A JOKE! I'VE A FEELING SHE'S THE NEW GIRL.

BILLIE MOSS, AREN'T YOU? COME IN AND MEET THE OTHERS.

YEP, I'M BILLIE. CHARMED I'M SURE!

THIS IS JILL HUNT, KIM BLYE, MONICA TROLLHEIM —

BORED TO MEET YOU ALL. WHY I SHOULD WANT TO KNOW YOU DEADBEATS ESCAPES ME.

LOOK — ANTHEA'S ONLY TRYING TO BE FRIENDLY! WHAT MAKES YOU THINK YOU'RE SO WONDERFUL, MISS HIGH-AND-MIGHTY?

ME TENNIS, THAT'S WHAT! GOING TO TRY ME OUT?

SOMEONE GIVE US A RACKET AN' I'LL SHOW YOU WHAT THE GAME'S ALL ABOUT.

HUH! I'VE JUST FINISHED A HARD GAME, BUT I SHALL BEAT THIS GUTTERSNIPE IN STRAIGHT SETS, AND TAKE HER DOWN A PEG OR TWO!

E

Soon after —

I'LL BE SEEING YOU ALL. HOPE SOME OF YOU OTHERS'LL BE ABLE TO GIVE ME A BETTER GAME!

GAME SET AND MATCH TO BILLIE MOSS. LOVE SIX, SIX LOVE, SIX LOVE.

THAT'S WHAT I CALL A WALKOVER!

WHY, THE ARROGANT SO-AND-SO!

S-SHE ONLY BEAT ME BY MAKING ME MAD WITH HER COMMENTS! WHO SENT THAT SCRUFF HERE, ANYWAY? AND WHY'S SHE SO UNFRIENDLY?

LUCY RADCLIFF'S PAYING FOR HER TO STUDY HERE — REMEMBER HER, THE WIMBLEDON STAR OF THE FIFTIES?

BUT SHE WAS FAMOUS FOR HER SPORTSMANSHIP — SOMETHING THIS BILLIE MOSS OBVIOUSLY LACKS!

Meanwhile, inside —

SO THIS IS IT — HOME FOR THE NEXT FEW YEARS. ONE DAY, MY PORTRAIT'S GOING TO BE UP THERE. I'LL BE THE MOST FAMOUS PUPIL THEY EVER HAD, MORE FAMOUS EVEN THAN — EH?

YOU MUST BE BILLIE MOSS. WON'T YOU COME INTO MY STUDY, PLEASE?

YEAH, SURE. YOU THE PRINCIPAL?

YOU HAVE BEEN ACCEPTED ON THE RECOMMENDATION OF THE FAMOUS LUCY RADCLIFF. SHE ASSURES ME YOUR TENNIS IS OF THE HIGHEST STANDARD. THAT IS ALL I KNOW ABOUT YOU, BUT I'M SURE WE'LL GET TO KNOW EACH OTHER SOON.

ROOM FIVE HAS BEEN PREPARED FOR YOU. I HOPE YOU'LL SETTLE IN QUICKLY.

THANK YOU, 'MISS.

THE UNIFORM WITH MY 'NAME' IN IT. IT'S FUNNY SEEING BILLIE MOSS EVERYWHERE — IT'LL TAKE SOME GETTING USED TO!

I'M GLAD MUM AGREED TO ME COMING HERE UNDER A FALSE NAME. I WANT TO MAKE IT ON MY OWN AND NOT BE IN HER SHADOW ALL THE TIME. BUT NOBODY MUST SUSPECT, THAT'S WHY MY WHOLE STYLE AND APPROACH HAS TO BE DIFFERENT FROM HERS.

To my darling daughter Jane Radcliff

IT'LL BE DIFFICULT KEEPING UP THIS BIGHEADED AND NASTY ACT, BUT I'VE GOT TO. WITH A BAD REPUTATION, NOBODY'LL BE ABLE TO LINK ME WITH MUM!

LIKE THE ROOM, BILLIE? I DO HOPE YOU'RE SETTLING IN.

HUH, WHAT D'YOU WANT, ANTHEA?

WHATEVER HAPPENS, NOBODY MUST SEE THIS PICTURE OR THEY'LL RUMBLE WHAT I'M UP TO!

WOULD YOU LIKE TO COME DOWN TO TEA WITH ME? YOU DON'T KNOW YOUR WAY AROUND YET.

SHE'S SO PLEASANT. IT'S MAKING IT VERY DIFFICULT TO KEEP UP MY SURLY PRETENCE. PERHAPS IF I SAVED MY BAD BEHAVIOUR FOR THE TENNIS COURT — OTHERWISE LIFE HERE'LL BE AWFUL!

YES, WHY NOT. THE FACT THAT I'M THE BEST TENNIS PLAYER HERE DOESN'T PREVENT ME MIXING WITH THE REST OF YOU.

THAT'S THE SPIRIT. COME ON!

IS THAT THE RUFFIAN WHO BEAT YOU AT TENNIS BY GAMESMANSHIP, JILLY?

THAT'S RIGHT. I DON'T KNOW WHAT ANTHEA SEES IN HER. PEOPLE LIKE HER SHOULD NEVER BE ALLOWED IN THE ACADEMY.

I'VE CERTAINLY DONE A GOOD JOB OF MAKING MYSELF UNPOPULAR.

WHAT'S YOUR GAME, ANTHEA, SITTING WITH THAT BILLIE MOSS?

YOU'LL NEVER MAKE A GOOD PROFESSIONAL TENNIS PLAYER IF YOU LET WHAT HAPPENS ON THE COURT UPSET YOU SO MUCH, JILLY. BILLIE'S NEW HERE, WE CAN AT LEAST GIVE HER A CHANCE.

ANTHEA'S RIGHT, SHE'S HARDLY BEEN HERE MORE THAN A FEW HOURS.

JUST WAIT 'TIL YOU OTHERS COME UP AGAINST HER BAD ATTITUDE AND BACKHANDED REMARKS ON COURT!

I NEVER REALISED MY ACT WOULD HAVE SUCH AN EFFECT ON EVERYBODY. MAYBE I WAS OVERDOING IT AND I OUGHT TO BE A LITTLE MORE PLEASANT.

After tea —

THIS IS SUCH A BEAUTIFUL PLACE. IF ONLY MUM WASN'T SO FAMOUS, I COULD DROP ALL THE PRETENCE AND RELAX, BUT THE GIRLS'D PROBABLY RESENT ME EVEN MORE IF THEY KNEW WHO I WAS. HEY — WHAT'S THAT — AN OUTDOOR POOL?

60

So, a few minutes later —

HI, BILLIE! FANCY A GAME OF WATER POLO? YOU'LL FIND A COSTUME IN YOUR LOCKER. THEY THINK OF EVERYTHING HERE!

GREAT, I'D LIKE THAT.

JUST IN TIME, BILLIE. YOU CAN BE IN MY TEAM.

I NEVER THOUGHT ABOUT PLAYING ANYTHING OTHER THAN TENNIS. STILL, AT LEAST I WON'T HAVE TO KEEP UP MY 'BIGHEAD' IMAGE IN THIS GAME.

'FRAID I WON'T BE MUCH USE AT THIS, I ONLY EVER PLAYED IT ONCE.

I THOUGHT YOU'D BE THE GREATEST AT EVERYTHING.

NEVER MIND, WE ONLY PLAY FOR FUN. LET'S GET THE GAME GOING.

WELL BLOCKED, BILLIE.

I WAS JUST LUCKY TO GET A TOUCH!

At the end of the game —

HERE, BILLIE, CATCH!

WHAT THE? AAH — I'M GOING TO —

I'M MAKING A FOOL OF MYSELF, AREN'T I?

NEVER MIND, SEEMS YOU'RE NOT SUCH AN OGRE AFTER ALL, BILLIE. C'MON, TIME FOR A TENNIS SESSION.

I TOLD YOU IT WAS WRONG TO JUDGE PEOPLE BY FIRST IMPRESSIONS, JILL. WHEN A NEWCOMER ARRIVES AT A PLACE LIKE THIS, THEY CAN BEHAVE IN STRANGE WAYS. IT HAPPENS ALL THE TIME.

PERHAPS. BUT SHE SEEMS A DIFFERENT PERSON ON COURT — AS YOU'LL PROBABLY FIND OUT!

ANTHEA'S REALLY STUCK UP FOR ME EVER SINCE I ARRIVED, AND I DON'T WANT TO MAKE HER LOOK SMALL, BUT I MUST KEEP UP MY 'BAD GIRL' IMAGE ON COURT OR THEY MIGHT RECOGNISE MUM'S STYLE IN ME.

Later —

PRACTICE AND MORE PRACTICE — IT'S THE ONLY WAY I'LL BEAT MY MOTHER'S RECORD OF THREE WIMBLEDON TITLES.

SORRY TO INTERRUPT YOUR PRACTISING, BILLIE, BUT WE'VE FIXED UP A MATCH BETWEEN YOU AND ANTHEA. SHE'S ONE OF OUR BEST PLAYERS AND WE LIKE TO DO A BIT OF OUR OWN SEEDING HERE. OKAY?

WELL, I'D RATHER NOT.

63

Soon —

FASTER! TURN QUICKLY! PUT YOUR BACKS INTO IT!

WOW! I'VE NEVER DONE TRAINING LIKE THIS BEFORE, BUT IT'S BOUND TO SHARPEN MY REACTIONS!

YOU'RE A BIT ON THE SLOW SIDE, BILLIE. WE'RE GOING TO HAVE TO SPEED YOU UP A BIT.

SHE'S NOT SLOW WHEN IT COMES TO DODGY TACTICS ON COURT, THOUGH!

After lunch —

WE'RE A TEAM NOW — 'CONNOLLY' TEAM — AND I WANT YOU TO ACT AS SUCH. IF ONE GIRL STEPS OUT OF LINE IT REFLECTS ON ALL THE OTHERS. THIS AFTERNOON WE'RE INVOLVED IN A LOCAL COMPETITION...

...I KNOW IT'S SHORT NOTICE, BUT I DON'T BELIEVE IN HAVING BUILD-UPS TO GAMES. REMEMBER ALL COMPETITIONS ARE EQUALLY IMPORTANT. THIS IS THE KEY TO CONSISTENT PLAY.

THAT'S WHAT I BELIEVE, TOO — EVERY GAME IS IMPORTANT. THAT'S WHY I WANT TO WIN THEM ALL!

IT'S AN OPEN COMPETITION SO THERE'LL BE LOTS OF DIFFERENT TYPES OF PLAYERS.

GREAT — JUST WHAT I WANT. LOADS OF MATCH PRACTICE AND DIFFERENT STYLES!

THAT'S ENOUGH OF THAT TALK. WE ARE HERE TO PLAY AND IMPROVE OUR TENNIS. YOU MUST LEARN TO GET ON WITH PEOPLE AS WELL, OTHERWISE YOU WILL NOT MAKE A GOOD PLAYER!

ALL THE TEACHERS HERE SEEM TO BE VERY FAIR, SO MY PROBLEMS WITH THE OTHER GIRLS SHOULDN'T HOLD BACK MY TENNIS.

Billie won the first three rounds of the tournament, easily beating mediocre players —

SAY WHAT YOU LIKE ABOUT BILLIE, BUT SHE'S WINNING MATCHES FOR 'CONNOLLY'! THE TEAM WITH THE BEST RECORD EACH TERM WINS THE ACADEMY SHIELD.

I PLAY THAT GIRL WITH THE EYESHADE IN THE NEXT ROUND — BUT WHAT ARE HER PARENTS GOING ON ABOUT?

YOU MUST DO WELL IN THIS NEXT ROUND, JUNE, OR YOU CAN SAY GOODBYE TO BECOMING A TENNIS STAR. WE CAN'T AFFORD TO PAY FOR TRAINING ANYMORE.

DON'T WORRY, DAD. IF I WIN THIS TOURNAMENT I'LL ALSO WIN THE SCHOLARSHIP TO ROSEWELL!

THE GIRL'S FUTURE DEPENDS ON HER BEATING ME. W-WHAT SHALL I DO?

I WANT TO WIN — FOR MYSELF AND THE TEAM. BUT HER WHOLE LIFE DEPENDS ON THIS!

COME ON, BILLIE, WIN THIS AND OUR TEAM BEATS ALL THE OTHERS ON POINTS!

YOU PRETENDED TO INJURE YOUR LEG BACK THERE SO THE GIRL RELAXED HER CONCENTRATION, THEN DESTROYED HER. THAT'S PRETTY MEAN.

THERE'S NO POINT IN TRYING TO EXPLAIN MY SIDE OF THINGS TO ANTHEA — SHE'S JUST NOT INTERESTED.

HUH! BILLIE'S REDUCED HER OPPONENT TO TEARS. I'D RATHER GIVE UP TENNIS THAN WIN LIKE THAT!

SEEMS I CAN'T DO ANYTHING RIGHT. I'M GETTING STICK FOR WINNING — BUT IF I'D LOST, THEY'D HAVE SAID I'D LET THE TEAM DOWN.

ANTHEA SAW ME EARLIER WITH MY MUM'S PHOTOGRAPH. SHE MUST HAVE GUESSED WHO I AM — BUT WHY HASN'T SHE LET ON TO THE OTHERS YET?

YOU WEREN'T VERY IMPRESSIVE IN TRAINING, BILLIE. BUT YOU CERTAINLY PLAYED WELL OUT THERE. HOW'S YOUR LEG?

OH, IT—IT'S ALL RIGHT NOW.

ASK HER HOW HER BIG HEAD IS, MISS.

WHAT? WHO SAID THAT?

YOU SHOULD BE ASHAMED OF YOURSELVES, GIRLS — SUCH PETTINESS. THANKS TO BILLIE,OUR TEAM WON.

LUMME! SHE'S TRYING TO STICK-UP FOR ME BUT SHE'S ONLY MAKING THINGS WORSE.

But —

MY—MY PURSE — IT'S GONE! IT'S BEEN STOLEN! AND—AND I HAD ALL MY POCKET MONEY FOR THE TERM IN IT!

COME ON, GIRLS — LET'S LOOK FOR TRUDY'S PURSE!

IT'S NO USE, MISS — IT'S JUST NOT HERE. WE'VE SEARCHED EVERYWHERE.

DON'T WORRY, TRUDY — WE'LL REPORT IT TO THE POLICE.

Then —

LOOK AT THE ROSEWELL LOT. ANYONE'D THINK THEY'D LOST. WHAT A BUNCH OF MISERIES!

Later, back at school —

SINCE NO ONE'S LIKELY TO TALK TO ME, I MAY AS WELL GO DOWN TO THE GYM —

RIGHT, BILLIE — OWN UP. YOU STOLE THAT PURSE, DIDN'T YOU?

EH? WHAT'RE YOU TALKING ABOUT? I'M NO THIEF!

Then as Jilly watched —

NO? THEN HOW COME YOU HAD A PHOTOGRAPH BELONGING TO LUCY RADCLIFF'S DAUGHTER?

DON'T BE RIDICULOUS. THAT PHOTO WAS — WAS GIVEN TO ME BY JANE RADCLIFF HERSELF.

YOU DO BELIEVE ME, DON'T YOU?

WELL, I CAN'T PROVE OTHERWISE. BUT IT DOES SOUND A BIT FAR-FETCHED.

GOOD! THERE'S A GAME OF SQUASH GOING ON. MAYBE I CAN JOIN IN LATER — I NEED TO SHARPEN MY REFLEXES.

WHAT A STROKE OF LUCK! THAT MEANS ANTHEA HASN'T GUESSED I'M JANE RADCLIFF.

Rosewell Academy

YOU CAN SAY THAT AGAIN!

But no one wanted to play with Billie —

WHAT A BORE! BUT ONCE I'VE GOT THIS OUT OF THE WAY I CAN GET AN EARLY NIGHT.

Later, as she was about to fall asleep —

SOMEONE AT MY DOOR. WHAT NOW?

THINK I HAD THE PLAGUE OR SOMETHING THE WAY THEY'RE ALL TREATING ME. OH, WELL, MAY AS WELL GET SOME STUDYING IN.

WHAT'S THIS, JILLY — A DEPUTATION?

YEAH, YOU COULD SAY THAT. CAN I HAVE A WORD WITH YOU IN PRIVATE?

However –

RIGHT I KNOW YOU PINCHED TRUDY'S PURSE, BUT I WON'T TELL ANYONE IF YOU COME INTO TOWN AND PLAY AGAINST WENDY DADE, THE PROFESSIONAL IN AN ALL-COMERS CHALLENGE MATCH.

WHAT? B–BUT I DIDN'T TAKE TRUDY'S PURSE!

BILLIE'S AGREED – AND IF ANYONE CAN BEAT WENDY DADE, BILLIE CAN!

BIT OF A BACKHANDED COMPLIMENT THAT. BUT I'VE GOT TO GO ALONG WITH JILLY – I DON'T WANT TO STIR UP MORE TROUBLE FOR MYSELF.

BUT I DON'T UNDERSTAND WHAT JILLY HOPES TO GET OUT OF ALL THIS. I MEAN, WHY WOULD SHE WANT ME TO BEAT WENDY DADE?

WHAT'S THIS THEN – ANOTHER HOPEFUL OUT TO WIN SOME MONEY AND GLORY?

MONEY? WHAT MONEY?

IT'S ME NEXT. ANYONE WHO TAKES A SET OFF WENDY STANDS TO WIN A HUNDRED POUNDS. CAN THAT BE WHAT JILLY'S AFTER – ALL THAT MONEY?

THERE'S MISS DADE! ISN'T SHE FABULOUS? AND SO FRIENDLY. SUCCESS HASN'T GONE TO HER HEAD!

I DAREN'T BEAT HER – OR THERE'LL BE SUCH A SPLASH IN THE PAPERS, THE TRUTH ABOUT ME COULD COME OUT.

THANKS FOR THE GAME, WENDY. CAN I HAVE YOUR AUTHOGRAPH?

OH, DROP DEAD! WHO'S NEXT FOR THE SLAUGHTER?

IF IT WASN'T FOR ALL THE LOVELY MONEY THE SPONSORS OF THIS FARCE ARE PAYING, I WOULDN'T BE SEEN DEAD IN THIS DUMP. I SUPPOSE YOU'RE ANOTHER NO-HOPER, EH?

WHAT A NASTY, HORRIBLE PERSON!

THANK YOU, FANS. I THINK I'M GOING TO HAVE MY HANDS FULL WITH MY NEXT OPPONENT. SHE SAYS I'M NOT ALL I'M CRACKED UP TO BE. WELL, WE'LL SEE.

EH? I DIDN'T SAY ANYTHING OF THE SORT. SHE'S JUST SAYING THAT TO GET THE CROWD AGAINST ME. WELL, FOR THAT I'M GOING TO BEAT HER – AND HANG THE CONSEQUENCES!

IF THAT PHOTOGRAPHER TAKES MY PICTURE MY SECRET WILL BE OUT. SOMEHOW I'VE GOT TO KEEP MY FACE AWAY FROM HIM. PERHAPS IF I PLAY MORE BACKHANDS —

THIS ISN'T MUCH USE — SHE'S KNOCKING ME ALL OVER THE COURT. GUESS THERE'S NO WAY I CAN WIN, NOW.

WOW, THIS'LL MAKE A GREAT STORY! THAT'S THE STYLE YOU NEED FOR THE BIG TIME.

THIS IS GETTING OUT OF HAND. WE'LL BE EXPELLED IF WE DON'T MOVE FAST.

OKAY, STAND STILL AND I'LL GET IT NOW.

LOOK, MATE, IF YOU WANT MY PICTURE THAT'S FINE, ONLY YOU'RE PUTTING ME OFF MY GAME!

NO, NOT YET. I'M IN A BIT OF A MESS. LET ME GO AND FIX MY HAIR FIRST.

WELL! I'VE NEVER SEEN THE LIKES BEFORE. GET ON WITH THE GAME, YOU LITTLE MADAM!

OH DON'T BE SUCH A DRIP, TRUDY!

But as the pressmen surged into the dressing-room.

SH—SHE'S GIVEN US THE SLIP!

C'MON, WE'VE WAITED LONG ENOUGH. BILLIE'LL HAVE TO LOOK OUT FOR HERSELF. OH, OH —

WHERE'RE THOSE GIRLS SHE WAS WITH? THERE'S A REALLY GREAT STORY HERE — I CAN SENSE IT!

THIS IS THE LAST BUS TO THE VILLAGE. IF WE MISS IT —

NO NEED TO BARGE, JILL, WE'LL ALL GET ON!

CONTINUED ON PAGE 98

ANIMAL MAGIC

DOLLS – rows and rows of them, with their little wax and china faces peering out from the musty shelves of the toy museum. Each small toy looking eager to tell its own particular story, if it only knew how.

By learning just a little about these early dolls, it is possible to know at least a part of that story.

wonder at. Their hair carefully braided with hand – painted clay beads which reflected the fashion of the day.

For the most doll-minded people in the world, we must travel to Japan. The artistic Japanese are famous for their beautiful display dolls, dressed exquisitely in silks and satins, often depicting an ancient dance or characters from history.

Living DOLLS

The first dolls known to man were most probably carved idols for temple worship, made in the likeness of various gods and fashioned from clay, stone and wood, whilst the coming of the Iron Age produced a glittering shower of dolls in bronze and other metals.

Every country in the world has a history of doll-making dating back hundreds and hundreds of years. In Greece, for instance, the same word is used for 'girl' as for 'doll'.

It is known that the Greek girls played with dolls right up until they married, when they would dedicate them, along with their other toys, to one of the Greek deities such as Aphrodite. The boys dedicated their toys to Apollo or Hermes.

The children from ancient Egypt would play with dolls stuffed with papyrus culled from the banks of the Nile. Many of these dolls are still carefully preserved on the museum shelves for visitors to

In modern homes today, the Japanese still teach the origin of their family by using these display dolls. They are always very carefully handled because they are handed down in the family for many centuries from mother to eldest daughter.

The dolls are brought out only once a year, placed on a special table and arranged in tiers which represent each stage and rank of that particular family. Thus the Japanese children learn all about the history of their household.

Images

English dolls, too, have stories to tell of bygone characters. In Queen Victoria's time it was fashionable for families to make images of local figures to be placed under glass domes on the mantlepiece, especially of pedlar women, who roamed from village to village carrying news and gossip, as well as a large tray of laces, medicines, pots and pans and other interesting and necessary wares.

It is not known why pedlars were singled out as the target for doll-makers. Perhaps the fact that many pedlars were thought to be witches fired the imagination of those Victorian needlewomen, or maybe the bright variety of the tray of wares challenged their skill.

The fact remains that chosen she was, and every item on her tray slavishly copied in miniature. Often, the wares would be made by the children of the household during long winter evenings when they were unable to go out to play.

In well-to-do families, the doll representing the pedlar was often bought, but in some poorer families it would be hand-made using an apple on a wooden skewer for the head.

The apple is dipped in vinegar, containing a dash of salt, then dried for three to six weeks in the open air until hard and leathery, when it can be painted, placed on a wire body and dressed in the traditional bonnet, print dress, white apron and red cape.

Sometimes, old and rare dolls are passed down in a family as heirlooms. If you are lucky enough to have one in your family, great care should be taken to keep it in good condition. Any china parts can be washed very carefully and very gently with mild soap and water.

Perhaps, like most people, you have no rare dolls in your family, but if you care for your own toys they will one day become just as rare as the little playthings on the shelves of the toy museum, and people will look and wonder what stories they could tell about the times in which they were made – and about you, the owner.

BESSIE BUNTER

"VOTE FOR STACKERS AS MAYOR!"

"MISS STACKPOLE, WE ARE DELIGHTED THAT YOU HAVE AGREED TO STAND AS A CANDIDATE FOR MAYOR OF COURTFIELD!"

"WE'LL HELP YOU TO WIN, MISS!"

"THANK YOU! IF I AM ELECTED, I WILL GIVE EACH GIRL A TEMPORARY JOB ON THE COUNCIL, SO THAT MY PUPILS CAN SEE HOW COUNCILLORS WORK!"

"HUH! WHAT'S THAT YOU'VE GOT, MARY MOLDSWORTH?"

"A LIST OF JOBS WHICH HAVE TO BE FILLED ON THE COUNCIL, BESSIE!"

"CATERING OFFICER FOR COURTFIELD! CRUMBS, IF I HELP TO GET STACKERS ELECTED, SHE'S BOUND TO GIVE ME THAT JOB!"

"WE'LL GO FROM HOUSE TO HOUSE AND SEE WHO IS LIKELY TO VOTE FOR THE HEAD, BESSIE!"

"RIGHT! I'LL CALL HERE!"

"DEAR ME! BESSIE HAS BEEN INSIDE FOR NEARLY AN HOUR...AH, HERE SHE COMES NOW!"

"WELL, ARE THEY FOR US OR AGAINST US?"

"PUT 'EM DOWN AS "DON'T KNOW". THEY ASKED ME TO HAVE TEA WITH THEM AND I FORGOT TO ASK!"

"REALLY, BESSIE! I THOUGHT YOU WOULD BE MORE INTERESTED IN DRUMMING UP SUPPORT FOR OUR HEAD!"

"DRUMMING UP! YOU'VE GIVEN ME AN IDEA, MARY!"

NEXT MORNING....

MISS STACKPOLE FOR MAYOR

"ROLL UP! ROLL UP! STACKERS FOR MAYOR!"

"HEY THERE! YOU'RE HOLDING UP THE TRAFFIC! GET OFF THE HIGH STREET AT ONCE!"

"HE MUST BE ON THE OTHER SIDE!"

"THANK YOU FOR YOUR EFFORTS, GIRLS, BUT YOU WOULD DO MORE GOOD IF YOU HELD SOME OPEN-AIR MEETINGS!"

"THAT'S AN IDEA!"

SO THAT AFTERNOON...

"FRIENDS, ROMANS, COUNTRYMEN, LEND ME YOUR EARS. I KNOW THAT YOU WILL VOTE FOR OUR PARTY..."

Wee Sue

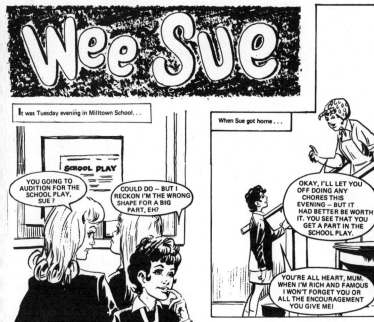

It was Tuesday evening in Milltown School...

SCHOOL PLAY

YOU GOING TO AUDITION FOR THE SCHOOL PLAY, SUE?

COULD DO — BUT I RECKON I'M THE WRONG SHAPE FOR A BIG PART, EH?

When Sue got home...

OKAY, I'LL LET YOU OFF DOING ANY CHORES THIS EVENING — BUT IT HAD BETTER BE WORTH IT. YOU SEE THAT YOU GET A PART IN THE SCHOOL PLAY.

YOU'RE ALL HEART, MUM. WHEN I'M RICH AND FAMOUS I WON'T FORGET YOU OR ALL THE ENCOURAGEMENT YOU GIVE ME!

GOT TO GET THESE LINES RIGHT, IF I'M TO PASS THE AUDITION. THIS BOOK MUST NOT BE RE-SOLD OR LENT — OOPS, WRONG LINES!

Later...

ASK NOT FOR WHOM THE BELL TOLLS...

Much later...

...THE BELL — DING DONG...

THE POOR DEAR, SHE'S FALLEN ASLEEP. SHE TAKES IT ALL SO SERIOUSLY. I'VE NEVER THOUGHT SHE'D BE CUT OUT FOR THIS ACTING STUFF.

Next day...

THANK YOU, SUE. TEN OUT OF TEN FOR EFFORT BUT — ER — NOT QUITE WHAT I'M LOOKING FOR. TELL YOU WHAT THOUGH, I'D LIKE YOU IN OUR LITTLE DRAMA AS AN UNDERSTUDY.

JUST WHAT I SUSPECTED. AH, WELL, SUPPOSE IT'S BETTER THAN NOTHING.

HOW DID IT GO, SUE. OH, I SEE —

THAT'S RIGHT — THE END OF A VERY PROMISING CAREER.

I TAKE IT NONE OF YOU WILL BE APPEARING IN THE RIDICULOUS SCHOOL PLAY WITH THAT UPSTART OF A MISS BROWN? OR ARE THERE SOME BUDDING THESPIANS AMONG MY LITTLE FRIENDS?

I FORGOT THAT MISS BIGGER HATES MISS BROWN'S GUTS. THIS IS GOING TO BE AWKWARD, BUT I'D BETTER SPEAK UP AND GET IT OVER WITH!

ER, I DON'T KNOW ABOUT THAT MISS, BUT MISS BROWN WANTS ME TO BE AN UNDER-STUDY IN THE SCHOOL PLAY. SO I WOULD APPRECIATE IT IF I COULD HAVE THE APPROPRIATE TIME OFF?

OH, YOU WOULD, WOULD YOU? I GET IT, NO PLUM PART FOR YOU — BUT PLENTY OF TIME OFF, THOUGH? WHAT D'YOU THINK THIS IS — A REST HOME FOR TIRED-OUT MIDGETS? NO YOU CAN'T!

BUT, MISS, IT'S NOT LIKE THAT . . . I WON'T NEGLECT ME LESSONS . . .

I'M NOT SUGGESTING FOR A MOMENT THAT YOU ARE USING THIS AS AN EXCUSE TO SPEND TIME AWAY FROM LESSONS. NOT AT ALL, I JUST DON'T WANT YOU WASTING YOUR PRECIOUS OPPORTUNITY OF A DECENT EDUCATION. HAVE YOU DONE YOUR HOMEWORK?

YOU FORGOT YOUR HOMEWORK — IT SPEAKS FOR ITSELF. I'M AFRAID THAT MEANS NO ACTING CAREER FOR YOU. I DO HATE TO DAMPEN YOUTHFUL ENTHUSIASM OR SEE MISS BROWN HAVING TO DO WITHOUT A VALUABLE UNDERSTUDY — BUT NO TIME OFF!

THANK YOU, MISS, I KNOW YOU HAVE MY BEST INTERESTS AT HEART!

MISS BIGGER HAS BEEN PRETTY NASTY — NASTIER THAN USUAL. PERHAPS THIS LETTER WILL PUT HER IN HER PLACE.

BREAK WILL SOON BE OVER, THEN SHE'LL COME IN AND READ THIS. I CAN ONLY HOPE IT WORKS OR THERE'LL BE A REAL DRAMA IN HERE!

SO I SAID TO HER, I SAID . . . WELL . . .

GOOD, SHE'S READING IT.

I'VE CHANGED MY MIND ABOUT THE — ER — THE PLAY, SUE STRONG. I'VE HAD SECOND THOUGHTS. YOU DO SEEM TO BE SET ON THIS ACTING, SO . . . IN OTHER WORDS YOU CAN HAVE TIME OFF TO ATTEND THE REHEARSALS.

OH, THANK YOU VERY MUCH, MISS.

So . . .

MISS BIGGER HAS ALLOWED ME TIME OFF TO WORK ON MY UNDERSTUDY PART AND SHE SAYS WHAT A MARVELLOUS THING IT IS THAT YOU HAVE TIME TO PUT ON A PLAY.

REALLY? THAT IS ENCOURAGING. GLAD TO HAVE YOU WITH US, SUE. WE NOW HAVE A COMPLETE UNDERSTUDY CAST AND YOU WILL REHEARSE THE PLAY ALONG WITH THE ACTUAL CAST.

. . . THE KING WILL NOT ABIDE IT. OUR FORCES WILL BE OVERWHELMED . . .

ER . . . IS THAT IN THE SCRIPT? SORRY I MUST'VE MISSED MY CUE.

IT'S NOT REALLY CONVINCING, SUE. YOU'VE GOT TO BELIEVE IN WHAT YOU SAY — REALLY GET INTO THE LINES!

I – I'LL TRY, MISS.

Reindeer

As the first few Christmas cards tumble through your letterbox, you might expect to see among their brightly-illustrated greetings a picture of a reindeer, because reindeers have become as familiar to us at this time of year as Santa Claus himself.

But pause to ask yourself, what do you know about reindeers? Do they really pull sledges? To find the answers to these and many more questions, you must follow the trail of the famous arctic explorers to the icy wonderland of the North Pole.

So put on your warmest clothes and come with me to this snow-clad hideaway at what may be truly termed the "top of the world", in search of one of the best-loved of all polar animals.

The reindeer (or caribou, as they are known in their wild state in North America) have roamed the snowy plains of the Arctic Circle for many hundreds of years, travelling in vast herds to afford greater protection from attack by wolf packs, their main enemy.

Roundabout

More recently, a nomadic people called the Lapps, who occupy parts of Norway, Sweden, Finland and Russia, have domesticated the reindeer, and today in these areas there are no wild herds to be found.

The reindeer is everything to the Lapps that the buffalo is to the American Indian, providing food, clothing and many other articles of use to them in their everyday life. In return, the Lapps protect the reindeer from predators and help to find food for the herd during the lean months of winter.

While the Lapp children are still young, they are given reindeer of their own and by a series of ear markings, each member if the family is able to recognise their particular creature among the herd. When the children grow up and marry, the reindeer belonging to the boy and girl will be pooled to form a new herd.

Reindeer are very well adapted to the cold climate of the polar region. They have soft fur in shades from creamy white to a warm brown, the hairs of which are hollow to hold the warmth of the animal's body for longer. Their hooves are rather special too, emitting a kind of "anti-freeze" fluid which keeps them from clogging up with snow, and they're big and flat to enable them to paw and dig the ground for the soft pale green spongy moss which is their main source of food during winter months.

Both male and female deers have antlers, the male antlers being substantially larger than that of the female. These are shed once a year, leaving two stubbly knobs where the magnificent multi-pronged horns once were. But they grow again very quickly and each year become a size bigger.

Reindeer Roundabout

At the first approach of spring, the reindeer get very restless, and by late April the Lapp family will harness their draught reindeer to the big sledges that carry all their worldly possessions, and take the ancient trail to their summer camp, which may well be some 200 miles away.

At one time, the Lapps would take the whole family on the migration, but as civilisation advances and more schools spring up in the area, it is usual for the women and children to stay behind.

Three types of reindeer sledges are used on this mammoth annual journey: the big high-backed sledge, for carrying food and equipment etc., and the light "pulka" type, shaped like a boat and with a keel instead of runners. The pulka is for travelling long distances on the plain and requires a lot of skill to manoeuvre it.

Thirdly, there would be a sledge with no back to it at all. This is the most important, for it carries the tent equipment and poles, which will drag out at the back of the sledge. The tent is essential for keeping out the sub-zero winds when the party stops on the trail for a rest.

The reindeer prefer to travel overnight when the snow is harder and the sledges easier to pull, so the Lapps set off in the evening when the sun starts to sink behind the hills, turning the snow to a vivid blood red.

The sledges swish through the stillness of the night until the early hours of the morning, when the travellers will strike camp and sleep the hours of daylight in their cosy home-made tents lined with reindeer skins.

It will be many days before they reach their destination and the way will be paved with unseen hazards, but the Lapps and their reindeer have travelled the old trails many, many times and set out well prepared.

A reindeer herd will move to the mountains or to the coast as summer approaches, to be rid of the mosquitoes and gadflies which lay their eggs in their fur. The larvae hatch, then burrow under the deer's skin, causing discomfort and loss of weight.

When they arrive on the summer ranges, the female deer will start to calve. Almost as soon as it is born, the baby reindeer struggles to take its first faltering steps, encouraged by the anxious and attentive mother. It looks a daunting task to get all four of its spread-eagled legs upright at the same time, but the urge to stand is as instinctive in the baby as it is in any wild animal. Week by week, the gawky youngsters grow strong, until autumn comes, bringing with it the "rut", when the adult deers choose a mate and also the herd's leader.

Quite soon, the ice on the lakes will begin to harden and winds that skim their surface take on a chilling sharpness. Both the reindeer and the Lapps know it is time to return once more to the winter camp. The youngsters of the herd, now quite sturdy, will need all their strength to swim the icy waters on their way to a home they have yet to see.

They will return again when the green moss dries and the first breath of spring catches their nostrils and tugs at their memory, to add a new circle to the age-old reindeer roundabout.

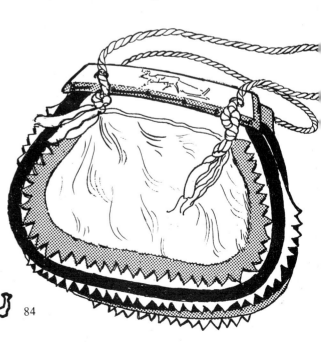

Pictures Of Peril

ANOTHER STRANGE STORY

CAN THE FUTURE ACTUALLY BE SEEN? IT'S A PRETTY TALL ORDER TO BELIEVE BUT IT TOOK ONLY A FEW HOLIDAY SNAPS TO CONVINCE AMATEUR PHOTOGRAPHER SANDRA WADE...

Sandra and her friend Jean had arrived on holiday in Cornwall.

WHAT A GREAT PLACE TO STAY. YOU'LL BE ABLE TO GET SOME SMASHING PHOTOS ROUND HERE, SANDRA.

I KNOW, JEAN. AND THE LANDLADY'S LETTING ME USE THE LINEN CUPBOARD FOR DEVELOPING.

OH, NO! WHAT A STUPID FOOL I AM! I'VE GONE AND LEFT MY FILM BEHIND.

NEVER MIND — LET'S GO DOWN TO THE BEACH. I WANT A SWIM AND YOU CAN GET SOME FILM IN A VILLAGE SHOP.

LOOK! THERE'S THE SHOP.

LOOKS LIKE THE ONLY SHOP IN THE VILLAGE. BET IT DOESN'T SELL FILM.

FILM? DON'T HAVE MUCH CALL FOR THAT ROUND HERE— BUT HANG ON AND I'LL HAVE A LOOK.

HE'D BE LUCKY IF HE FOUND ANYTHING IN THIS PLACE. RECKON YOU'VE WON THE BET.

But—

YOU'RE IN LUCK, LASS— BUT I WON'T CHARGE YOU NOWT FOR THE FILM. MUST'VE BEEN HERE DONKEY'S YEARS AND MIGHT NOT WORK.

OH— THANKS SO MUCH!

HE WASN'T JOKING ABOUT THIS BEING OLD. IT'S COVERED IN DUST AND LOOK AT THE STRANGE DESIGN ON IT.

PROBABLY SAYS MADE IN HONG KONG — NOW LET'S GET DOWN TO THE BEACH.

NOT COMING IN FOR A DIP TOO, SANDRA?

NO. YOU'RE THE ATHLETE — I'M THE PHOTOGRAPHER. I'LL TAKE SOME PHOTOS OF YOU.

HOLD IT. SMILE. THAT'S A GREAT SHOT.

IF THE FILM WORKS.

BUT WHAT IF IT'S GOING TO HAPPEN?

I TOLD HER NOT TO SWIM AFTER A MEAL BUT WHAT IF SHE IGNORED THAT?

I'VE GOT TO GET DOWN TO THE BEACH! THOSE PHOTOS WERE TAKEN IN FADING LIGHT... JUST LIKE IT IS NOW AT DUSK!

I CAN'T SEE HER — IT'S ALWAYS DARK OUT HERE! JEAN, JEAN!

SANDRA! OH, SANDRA! OVER HERE!

I'M COMING! I REMEMBER THE BIT OF SHORELINE IN THE PHOTOS! I KNOW WHERE YOU ARE!

IT'S ALL RIGHT, JEAN. I'VE GOT YOU NOW. YOU'RE SAFE.

THANK — THANK HEAVEN YOU FOUND ME.

Later.

IT WAS MY OWN STUPID FAULT GETTING CRAMP SWIMMING AFTER A MEAL ..IF IT HADN'T BEEN FOR YOU, SANDRA...BUT HOW DID YOU KNOW WHAT HAD HAPPENED? OR WHERE I WAS?

JUST A HUNCH.

LEAVING THE DARK-ROOM DOOR OPEN RUINED THOSE PHOTOS...SO I COULD NEVER PROVE IT, BUT SOMEHOW THAT STRANGE FILM TOOK PHOTOS OF THE FUTURE — AND WARNED ME JUST IN TIME.

ANIMAL
MAGIC

Are you looking good?

Take a look at these two girls. Which one do you identify with? They *could* be the same girl, but what a difference! Girl "A" is terribly overweight, stands badly and looks very miserable. Her hair is messy and she has spots on her face. She hides her hands because she bites her nails and never gives herself a manicure. Girl "B", on the other hand, stands well and watches her figure. She has her hair cut regularly, keeps it clean and shining, looks after her hands and looks happy! Which one are you? Even if you are somewhere between the two, this will help you to make the most of yourself and stay healthy.

first, watch your weight

Before anything else, check your weight. See your doctor if you think you are overweight, and he will give you a sensible diet sheet to follow that fits in with your age and way of life. Even if you are slim it's still a good idea to follow a sensible eating plan to keep your skin, hair and teeth looking good.

Try not to eat lots of fried food, fatty meat, chocolate and sweets, sugar, tinned foods, ice-cream and pasta. Eat less in the evening when you are less active, but eat a good breakfast.

> *Eat plenty of fresh fruit, vegetables, salads, lean meat, yogourt, eggs, fish, cheeses, wholemeal bread, bran, milk, some butter and margarine and drink lots of water.*

hair care

To keep your hair looking good and shiny, you should shampoo it at least once a week, more often if it is greasy. Try different shampoos, perhaps sharing the cost with a sister or friends and helping one another with washing and setting etc. Have a really good cut, this is very important. Keep brushes and combs clean and try using combs and hairslides to create new styles. Brush and comb well each night to keep your hair gleaming and healthy.

your clothes

Do you sometimes wonder what to choose when buying new clothes? And do you regret having bought something that just didn't go with anything else? We all make mistakes and learn the hard way! Sketched above are some ideas for getting a wardrobe together.

All the tops go with any of the "bottoms", and you'll have more than 25 outfits if you wear the cardigan and tee-shirt with other tops. Start off with a colour that suits you best and buy a shirt and toning skirt. Then, add other colours that "go" with them and build up a wardrobe from there. Add accessories like bags, belts, shoes and jewellery, and you'll look good!

your hands

One of the first things that people notice about you are your hands – especially if you try to hide them! If you give yourself weekly manicure and cream your hands every time you wash them, they will always look good. Soak your hands in warm soapy water (not detergent) for about five minutes. Use a soft nail brush necessary. File each nail with an emery board to just above tip of finger. Soak hands again. Using cuticle remover, gently push cuticle back with cotton wool wrapped in an orange stick. Rub a little cuticle all around nail. If you want to use nail varnish, choose natural or a pretty, pale shade and leave on for only a day or two. Gently dissolve with a good varnish remover. If you are a nail-biter, conquer the habit, or you'll never be admired for your hands!

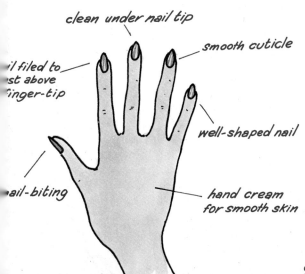

clean under nail tip

smooth cuticle

il filed to
st above
inger-tip

well-shaped nail

ail-biting

hand cream
for smooth skin

your face

It's no good looking pretty unless your skin looks good, too. Keep it clean with plenty of washing and deep cleansing with a cream at night. Use antiseptic cream on spots and a moisturiser in cold and windy weather.

Acne is often caused by over-greasy skin on young people. This sometimes has to be dealt with medically if it's severe, but you can help to avoid it by scrubbing the face gently with a soft nail brush and a good antiseptic soap.

Sun-tanning is something we all enjoy but have to be very careful about, otherwise we do more harm than good and look either very red and unattractive or peel and look even worse!

If you are fair-skinned, always start sunbathing five minutes at a time, even though you will feel impatient. After a few days, you can go out into the sun more freely, but always use sun prevention cream. And it's important to slip on a cool, cotton shirt at the first sign of burning. Those with darker skins still have to be careful, as they can burn, too.

Make-up is a subject that you will try for yourself and perhaps with a friend experiment together. Big stores are often very helpful and will let you try out their products and suggest the right colours. Keep to natural shades at first, and ask for samples where possible.

A "happy face" with sparkling eyes, rosy cheeks and gleaming white teeth will always make friends – and remember, the more YOU smile, others will follow!

If you're one of those girls who gets fed-up drawing or painting pictures, then . . .

Get that
FELT
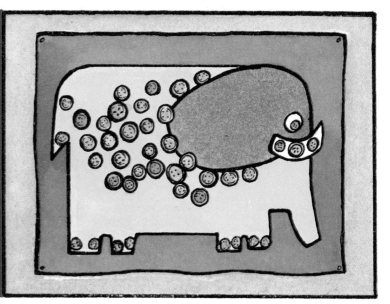

FEELING...

First, choose the design you want to make — it can be the one we suggest, or something completely different. Trace the various parts of your drawing on to the corresponding pieces of coloured felt, then cut out the pieces of felt, using a nice, sharp pair of scissors. Stick the pieces on to the background felt, using a transparent glue or gum (a very small amount is all that is necessary to stick one piece of felt to another).

FOR THIS ELEPHANT DESIGN, YOU WILL NEED:

Dark blue felt (62cms x 46cms), yellow felt (47cms x 35cms), white felt (10cms x 10cms) and brown felt (26cms x 18cms). Buttons of two different sizes (8 blue, 8 beige and 26 green). Blue, green and beige cotton. Special carbon transfer paper to mark the felt, glue and scissors.

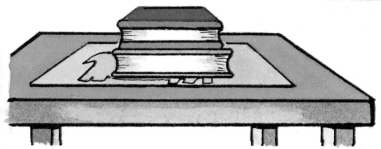

When the figure is made and in position, but before the buttons have been stitched on, it is a good idea to put the collage on a table with an even surface, putting some weight on top of it (a few books, for instance) for a few hours. This will press the pieces of felt firmly together. Finally, remove the weight and stitch on the buttons, making sure that the stitches go through all the pieces of felt to keep them securely together.

A PIN BOARD

um can pin notes or recipes on a board like this, Dad can pin his bills, your sister, her pop pics . . . in fact a pin board has ts of uses, is quite simple to make — but very expensive to buy!

For a pin board like this you will need a large polystyrene tile (from do-it-yourself shops), some felt of the same size, a pipe cleaner and a few drawing pins.

nd the pipe cleaner in half.

2. Push the ends through the back of the tile, near a corner, so that about half the pipe cleaner is showing each side.

3. Bend up the ends and open the loop. Stick the felt on to the tile, lightly press in a few drawing pins and your pin board is ready to hang up and use.

Fancy dressing up?

Invitations to "Fancy-Dress" parties can lead you to a lot of expense if you have to resort to hiring a costume from an agency or pay a dressmaker to run one up. Here are some ideas for you to create an outfit from garments and items you may already have, or can borrow. Even if you find you have to buy something new, it could be something you will wear again, like the leotards or cowboy boots.

GIPSY: Bright and colourful garments such as embroidered blouse, full gathered skirt with border design, small pinny, scarf, bolero and lots of bangles and beads. Wear a full petticoat under the skirt to give it more swing, and add a beribboned tambourine for an authentic finishing touch.

SOUTH SEA ISLANDER: Start off with a bikini top or "boob-tube" Add a "grass skirt" made from garden raffia stitched to a waistband or cut strips of coloured crêpe paper, using about three layers. Make coloured paper flowers and attach to wrists and ankles using elastic bands. Pin one to either side of hair and string some into a garland or "Lei" as they call them in Hawaii.

LUCKY BLACK CAT: Black leotards from a keep-fit student, plus tights, worn together with mitts, perhaps left over from a ski-ing holiday. The head can easily be made from a boy's balaclava helmet or from a tube of black jersey pulled over the head. Two "ears" can be made by pulling out and tying some of the jersey or making separate pieces and sewing them onto the hat. Paint lines on face for "whiskers". Tail is long tube of jersey or leg of old tights or stockings, stuffed and sewn on seat of leotard.

COW GIRL: Borrow a young brother's cowboy-hat and toy rifle. Find a check shirt, and a scarf to knot at your neck. The waistcoat and skirt you can fringe at the edges, or sew on matching or white fringing. Buy or borrow some boots. (cowboy-style look best), and take along the rifle, lasso or strap a holster around your waist.

CLOWN: Cut two shapes, using diagram as a guide. This you can colour with fabric paints or felt-tips. Sew together, leaving neck, cuffs and ankles open, then gathering with elastic. Sew on frill and pom-poms, adding cone-shaped hat.

TURKISH DELIGHT: Cotton scarf and hankie make a yashmak and head-dress. Bikini top and pyjama-style trousers covered with sequins, can be finished off with a brightly coloured tie. Wind gold or silver Christmas gift ribbon around ankles. Wear lots of bright bangles, too!

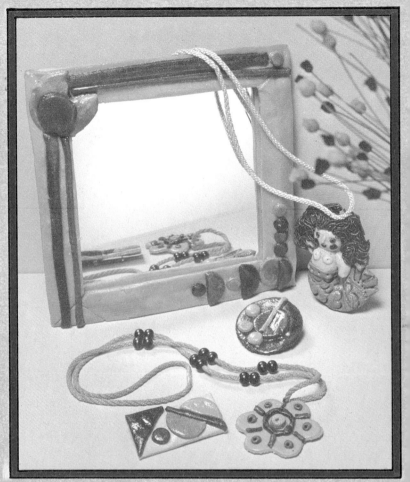

DO you want to make some unusual presents for family or friends, brighten up your clothes for the party season, or have something handy for the next fund-raising sale in your area?

If you do, we've a suggestion for you—find the flour and water! Yes, that's what the items in our picture are made of— ordinary flour and water mix, blended with "Dylon" Cold Dyes to give them those lovely, rich colours, then baked hard and coated with "Mr. Dylon" clear gloss polyurethane for a tough, chip-resistant finish. (You can buy all "Dylon" products from craft shops, department stores, and most hardware suppliers, including Woolworth's.)

Do it with Dough!

To make the brooches, pendants and mirror frame illustrated, you will need: $4\frac{1}{2}$ cups of plain flour; $1\frac{1}{2}$ cups of salt; Dylon Cold Dyes (we used Sahara Sun, Mexican Red and Bahama Blue); aluminium foil; biscuit cutters or small glasses; cocktail stick; garlic press or a coarse sieve to make the mermaid's hair; 2 brooch pins; fuse wire; lacing cord for the necklace; coloured beads; a small mirror or mirror tile; cardboard; a strong, clear adhesive, plus Mr. Dylon clear gloss polyurethane.

First, mix together the flour and salt, and put two cups of this mixture into a bowl. Dissolve the

yellow dye in $\frac{1}{2}$ litre (one pint) of warm water, add as necessary to the flour and salt, and knead into a firm dough with a fork. Once the dye has been well blended, the dough is clean on the fingers and can be rolled, cut and moulded like pastry!

Mix as before for the other colours, using $1\frac{1}{2}$ cups for the red and blue dyes, and 1 cup mixed with plain water for the white dough. Green can be made by blending together some of the blue and yellow dough, purple from the red and blue dough, and orange by mixing the red and yellow dough.

To begin making the jewellery, roll out some of the white,

yellow, red, purple and green doughs to ·3 cm, ($\frac{1}{8}$") thick.

For the rectangular brooch, cut a $2\frac{1}{2}$" × 1" (5 cm × 3 cm), rectangle from the white dough and place on aluminium foil. Decorate with shapes cut from the coloured doughs, sticking them in position with water. The circular brooch is made in the same way, first cutting the circle from the red dough with a biscuit cutter, or wine glass.

The scalloped pendant is made by cutting a flower shape from the yellow dough and placing on aluminium foil, as before. Then make a loop from fuse wire and push it into the top of the pendant. Pattern with small pieces of red, purple and green dough rolled between the fingers, and punch holes with a cocktail stick to complete the design.

To make the mermaid pendant, make a small ball for the head with white dough and a larger one for the top half of her body, then join together with water. Make a "sausage" from green dough, join to the body and model into the mermaid's tail, marking little scales with the cocktail stick. Place on aluminium foil.

Now, using white dough, roll out a thinner sausage, cut in half for her arms, and join to the body. Make the hair by pushing a small ball of orange dough through a garlic press or sieve. Insert a loop of fuse wire, and make a face for your mermaid by positioning tiny pieces of dough

with a cocktail stick, using white for the nose, red for the cheeks and purple for the eyes.

Bake hard in a slow oven set at the lowest temperature. This will take about 2–3 hours, with the things you've made placed on a baking sheet just above the centre of the oven. When cold, paint with Mr. Dylon clear gloss polyurethane and leave to dry. Glue on brooch pins with a strong adhesive and thread pendants on lacing cord, adding a few beads for extra decoration, if you want to.

The mirror frame can be made just as easily. First, draw round the mirror on to cardboard, cut out and cover with aluminium foil. Then place on more foil in the centre of a baking sheet. Roll out the yellow dough to the thickness of the mirror, and the

red, green and purple doughs ·3 cm ($\frac{1}{8}$") thick. Next, cut four yellow strips 1 cm, ($\frac{1}{2}$"), wide and place alongside the foil-covered cardboard, sealing the corner joins with dabs of water.

Cut another four strips 2·5 cm (1") wide, and place on top of first layer, overlapping the cardboard. Decorate the frame with thin strips and different size circles cut from the red, green and purple dough. Bake hard and paint with Mr. Dylon clear gloss polyurethane as before. When dry, glue frame to the mirror with clear, strong adhesive.

Don't worry about any pieces of left-over dough once you've finished your modelling session. These can be kept in a polythene bag in the fridge ready for use another time. So why not have a go, readers, and "dough" it yourself?

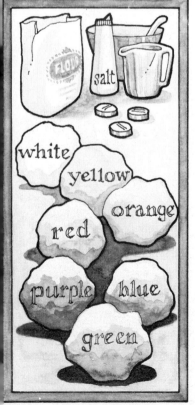

white
yellow
orange
red
purple blue
green

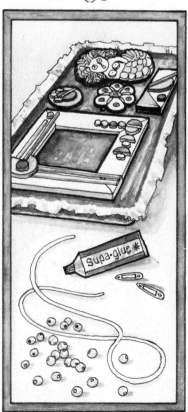

salt

Supa-glue

S—SORRY, MISS. I FANCIED SOME APPLES AND GOT STUCK UP THE TREE. BILLIE HELPED ME DOWN.

COME ALONG INSIDE, IT'S COLD TONIGHT.

YOU'RE BOTH NEW HERE, AREN'T YOU? IT'S AGAINST THE RULES TO BE IN THE GROUNDS AFTER LIGHTS-OUT, BUT I'LL OVERLOOK IT THIS ONCE.

WE WON'T BE — ER — PICKING ANY MORE APPLES! G'NIGHT, MISS.

THANKS A LOT, BILLIE. YOU STUCK BY ME WHEN JILL RAN. YOU'RE NOT AT ALL LIKE SHE SAYS YOU ARE!

I PUT JILL'S NOSE OUT OF JOINT AND MADE MYSELF POPULAR, BUT IT CAN'T LAST. MUM WAS ALWAYS THE 'NICE GUY' AND IF I GO THAT WAY THEY MIGHT SEE THE RESEMBLANCE. NO, I WANT TO BE A TOP PLAYER, AND I'VE GOT TO DO IT MY WAY!

WELL DONE, BILLIE. WE'VE HEARD ALL ABOUT IT — AND YOUR GAME WITH MISS DADE! YOU'RE A REAL CHARACTER!

WOW! WHAT A CHANGE! THEY ALL SEEM TO LIKE ME NOW.

Next morning, at practice...

LOOK AT THE WAY SHE'S HITTING THE BALL — WHAT CONFIDENCE.

GOOD, ISN'T SHE?

OH YEAH? WHAT DO YOU TWO DUFFERS KNOW ABOUT IT? I COULD LICK YOU BOTH WITH ONE HAND BEHIND ME BACK!

I—I HATE MYSELF! BUT I HAD TO DO IT. IT'S EITHER THAT AND BEING A GREAT PLAYER OR BEING JUST THE MOST POPULAR GIRL IN THE ACADEMY!

BIGHEAD! I DON'T KNOW WHY WE BOTHER TO TALK TO HER!

NO, PLEASE, BILLIE'S JUST TIRED AFTER WHAT HAPPENED —

AND WHO ASKED FOR YOUR ROTTEN OPINION? MIND YER OWN!

YOU'VE DROPPED YOURSELF IN IT NOW, BIG MOUTH! LET'S SEE YOU PLAY THOSE TWO WITH ONE HAND!

I CAN'T VERY WELL BACK-OUT NOW, BUT I'LL MAKE A REAL FOOL OF MYSELF. WHAT A MESS!

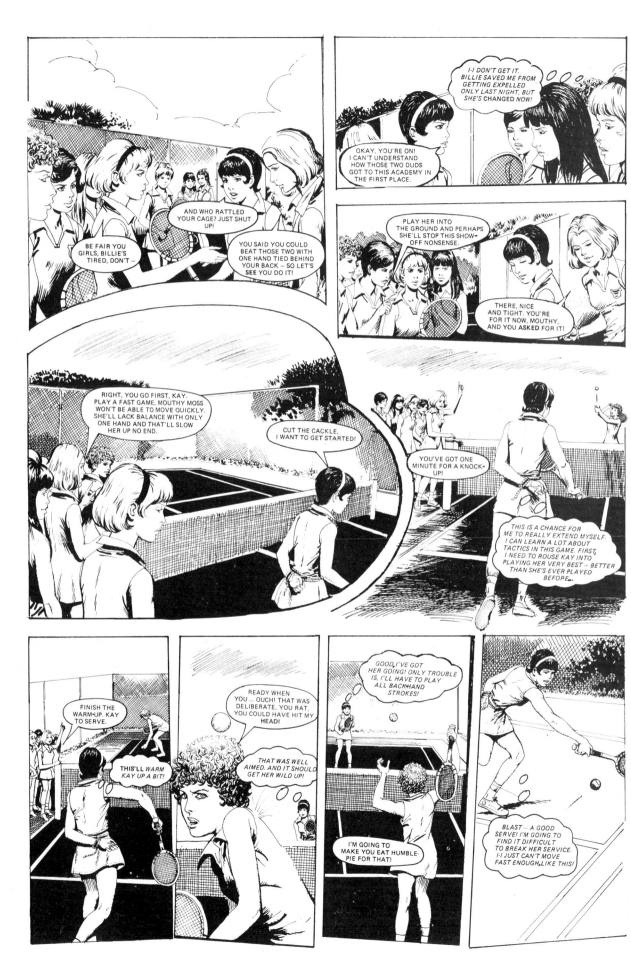

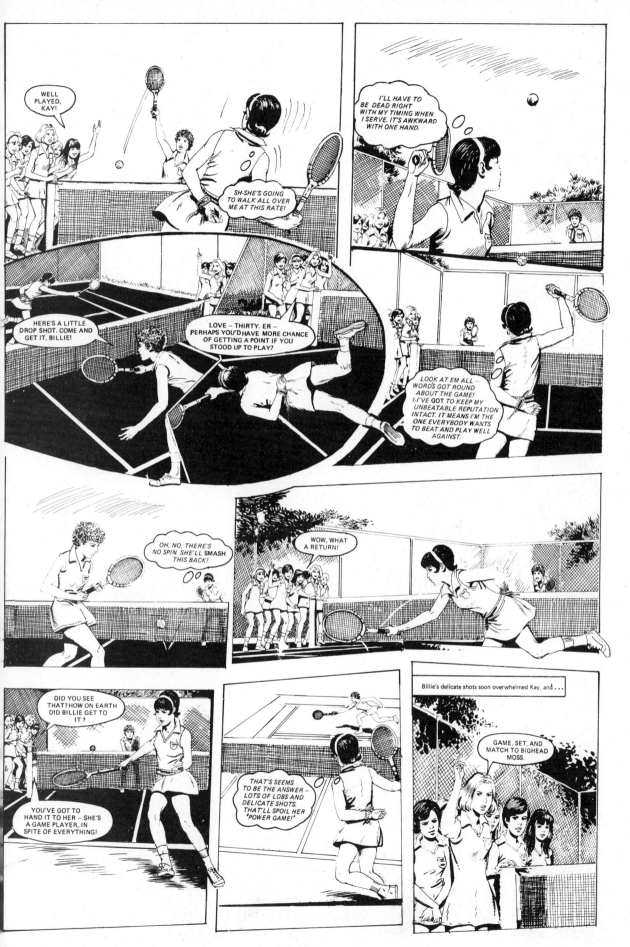

101

WAIT A MINUTE, SHE'S STILL TO TAKE ON ANN ONE-HANDED — THAT WAS THE DEAL!

FORGET IT I CAN BEAT HER **WITHOUT** ANY HANDICAPS, SHE'S NOT THAT GOOD.

After a few quick games...

ANN'S DONE IT, SHE'S CRACKED, BILLIE MOSS!

I SUPPOSE IT HAD TO HAPPEN SOME DAY. ANN'S TWIGGED ME.

I'VE BEEN WATCHING HER. HER BOASTING AND THAT'S ALL AN ACT SO THAT SHE CAN WORK HERSELF UP TO A STATE WHERE SHE PLAYS HER BEST. AND SHE DISTRACTS HER OPPONENT TO PUT THEM OFF **THEIR** GAME!

THIS IS THE FIRST TIME I'VE PLAYED WITHOUT ANY GIMMICKS — AND IT'S SHOWING!

THERE'S NO WAY I CAN MAKE ANN ANGRY. SHE'LL IGNORE MY REMARKS. I-I'LL NEED TO RETHINK MY GAME ENTIRELY!

WOW! THE FIRST SET TO ANN BY SIX GAMES TO TWO.

BILLIE'S FINISHED. SHE'S GOT NOTHING TO OFFER! SHE MIGHT AS WELL PACK HER BAGS AND GO HOME.

ANN LEADS THREE GAMES TO LOVE IN THE FINAL SET. AND LOOK HOW THE MIGHTY HAVE FALLEN!

LOOK AT THAT ROW OF FACES — THEY ALL WANT TO SEE ME HUMILIATED — NOT JUST BEATEN BUT **DESTROYED!**

YOU'RE RUBBISH, BILLIE MOSS!

I'LL NOT GIVE THEM THE SATISFACTION OF SEEING ME BEATEN, I DON'T **HAVE** TO HATE ANY MORE–I'LL TAKE A **PRIDE** IN WHAT I DO AND GIVE OF MY BEST ALL THE TIME!

YOUR NAME IS MOSS, ISN'T IT? TRY A NICE CLOD OF EARTH — YOU CAN TAKE ROOT ON IT!

HOW DO YOU LIKE BEING ON THE END OF POOR SPORTSMANSHIP?

ANN'S ONLY GOT TO HOLD HER SERVE TO WIN. AFTER THAT, IT'LL BE ALL OVER FOR BILLIE AND HER BACKHAND WAYS!

103

HA, THEY THOUGHT IT WAS ALL OVER, BUT IT'S ONE *SET* ALL NOW!

COME ON, ANN, YOU CAN DO IT. YOU'VE GOT HER MARK NOW, SHE'S JUST HAD A FEW LUCKY BREAKS, THAT'S ALL.

I RECKON YOU'RE THE ONLY ONE OF US WHO CAN BEAT HER! YOU'VE GOT TO DO IT, AND PUT THE BRAT IN HER PLACE. WHY, SHE'S SO BIGHEADED, WITH ANY LUCK, SHE MIGHT EVEN LEAVE THE ACADEMY!

I'VE GOT TO PULL MYSELF TOGETHER, I MEAN, I'VE NEVER BEEN BEATEN SINCE I JOINED THIS PLACE, SO I CAN'T BE THAT BAD!

STOP PLAYING FOR TIME, MOSS — OR CAN'T YOU TAKE BEING A LOSER?

But, as the match progressed —

EVERYTHING'S CLICKING FOR ME AGAIN. I SEEM TO HAVE FOUND MY FORM AT JUST THE RIGHT TIME. ANN'S GROUND-STROKES ARE VERY WEAK AND MY STRONG SERVES AND VOLLEYS ARE BEATING HER EVERY TIME!

HARK AT THEM JEERING ME AND ROOTING FOR ANN. I RECKON I COULD MAKE THIS GAME A BIT MORE LIVELY FROM THEIR POINT OF VIEW.

NOT BAD ACTING. THEY DIDN'T REALISE THAT 'DOUBLE FAULT' WAS DELIBERATE!

GO ON, ANN — YOU'VE GOT HER RATTLED NOW!

I'M THROWING THESE POINTS AWAY TO MAKE THE GAME MORE INTERESTING! HANGING BACK FROM THE NET TO LET ANN PLAY HER FAVOURITE LONG SHOTS, MAKES HER LOOK GOOD.

FIVE GAMES ALL, FINAL SET. YOU'VE ONLY TO HOLD YOUR SERVE AND BREAK BILLIE'S FOR THE MATCH, ANN!

THAT'S WHAT THEY THINK! I'VE MUCKED ABOUT FOR LONG ENOUGH. NOW TO SHATTER A FEW HOPES!

BLOW, THAT WAS A WEAK RETURN. STILL, I THINK I'LL SURPRISE HER WITH A DELICATE LOB!

YES! IT'S OUT!

BLAST! JUST WHEN I NEED TO BE DEAD ACCURATE, I MAKE SOME UNFORCED ERRORS!

Billie found herself struggling to hold her service next game —

WHAT A MATCH! YOU MUST ADMIT BILLIE'S GAME, BUT SHE JUST CAN'T BEAT ANN, NOW!

TH-THEY'RE RIGHT. SHE'S RETURNED ALL MY BEST SHOTS. I JUST CAN'T OUTWIT HER!

For Billie, who had never tasted defeat, it was a bitter moment —

THAT WAS A BIG POINT TO LOSE. ANN'S FULL OF CONFIDENCE NOW. I MUSTN'T LET IT UPSET ME, EVERY POINT'S VITAL AT THIS STAGE IN THE GAME!

WELL PLAYED! YOU'VE SHOWN THAT LOUD-MOUTH SHE'S NOT THE GREATEST!

I SHOULD NEVER HAVE PLAYED ABOUT LIKE THAT. I HAD HER IN MY GRASP AND COULD HAVE CRUSHED HER AT ANY TIME. I GAVE IT AWAY! AND AFTER I'D RESOLVED TO CHANGE MY ATTITUDE, TOO!

POST MORTEMS ARE ALWAYS INTERESTING, BILLIE. KNOW WHERE YOU WENT WRONG?

EH, WHO'S THAT?

It was Miss Ball, head of the academy —

NOW THAT YOU'VE STARTED TO THINK ABOUT YOURSELF AND YOUR GAME, YOU MAY BE IN A POSITION TO LEARN FOR THE FIRST TIME!

LEARN? I'VE LEARNT NOTHING SINCE I CAME HERE!

COME IN HERE, BILLIE. I'VE SOMETHING TO SHOW YOU. YOU'LL SOON SEE WHAT I MEAN.

A VIDEO SET! YOU MONITOR EVERY GAME WE PLAY. BUT WHY?

WE STUDY EVERY MOVE OUR PUPILS MAKE, THEN PLAY THEM BACK AT SLOW SPEED TO ANALYSE THEIR FAULTS. WHEN THEY ARE READY, WE TALK THEM THROUGH OUR FINDINGS AND TRY TO HELP THEM LEARN FROM THEIR MISTAKES. THIS METHOD HAS HELPED THE ACADEMY TURN OUT SOME TOP-CLASS PLAYERS!

BUT I DON'T NEED THAT! I CAN LICK ANYONE AT THIS PLACE. THAT GAME JUST NOW WAS A FLUKE, I'VE NEVER BEEN BEATEN!

110

Shape up to Sculpture!

Why not be inventive and experiment with sculpture?
Look at all the things illustrated here.
What can you make with them?

First, there's soap. Use a spoon to shape models
or designs. Candle wax models can be made
this way, too. You can paint the candle first.
Mix powder paint with washing-up liquid
to make a thick paint which will stick to a
candle. Paint wax, then cut your pattern into
the candle with a sharp teaspoon.

You can make a "twig sculpture" by using clay
and sticky tape, decorating it with foil or
milk bottle tops.

Many models can be made from cardboard.
Cut slits as required to join pieces together.
Paint in bright colours.

Vegetable animals

You can make "wire sculptures" with pipe
cleaners, and many an animal shape from
vegetables, sticks and nails.

Try making a "vegetable zoo!"

What's this?

ASK THE ARMSTRONG CHILDREN FROM MANCHESTER, WHO DESIGNED THESE QUIZ PICTURES.

LEMON-AID

TOOTH-PICK

BANANA-SPLIT

WINDOW-PAIN

TEA-CADDY

ROW-IN-BOAT

THE DEMON IN THE DOLL

ANOTHER STRANGE STORY

THE HEARTS OF MANY CITIES HAVE BEEN COMPLETELY DE-MOLISHED IN RECENT YEARS – TO MAKE WAY FOR MODERN SHOPPING PRECINCTS AND OFFICE BLOCKS. SOMETIMES THE DEMOLITION MEN UNEARTH SECRETS THAT SHOULD HAVE BEEN LEFT UNDISTURBED...

HEY, GANG! LOOK WHAT MY DAD FOUND ON A DEMOLITION SITE – AN OLD VICTORIAN DOLL. IT WAS BRICKED-UP BEHIND A FIREPLACE.

WHAT? I THOUGHT YOU WERE PAST THE STAGE OF SOPPY DOLLS, JUDY.

GIVE IT BACK, BILL – OR I'LL THUMP YOU.

I KNOW! WE'LL PLAY FOOTBALL WITH IT!

THANKS, JOHN. ISN'T SHE GORGEOUS? I THINK I'LL CALL HER VICTORIA!

GORGEOUS? I – I THINK SHE'S SPOOKY. I MEAN, WHY WOULD ANYONE WANT TO BRICK HER UP BEHIND A FIREPLACE?

LOOK – A HOLE FOR A KEY. PERHAPS SHE WALKS – OR TALKS?

GOSH! HOW EXCITING!

COME ON, JUDY – WE WERE GOING TO THE PICTURES, REMEMBER?

SORRY, BUT I DON'T FANCY IT ANYMORE. I WANT TO FIND A KEY TO FIT THE DOLL.

MY DAD'S GOT LOTS OF OLD KEYS IN HIS TOOL SHED. BET ONE OF THEM WOULD FIT IT.

COME ON, BILL – LET'S LEAVE THEM AND THEIR STUPID DOLL.

THERE! I KNEW ONE OF THEM WOULD WORK! LET'S SEE WHAT SHE DOES NOW.

OH, I – I CAN HARDLY WAIT!

GOOD MORNING. HOW ARE YOU? IT'S SUCH A LOVELY ... HELLO, GOOD MORNING. IT'S SUCH A LOVELY ... HELLO ...

WHAT A FUNNY LITTLE VOICE!

THERE'S SOMETHING WRONG WITH THE MECHANISM. SHE STOPS IN MID-SENTENCE THEN STARTS ALL OVER AGAIN.

STILL — SHE'LL LOOK LOVELY ON MY DRESSER BACK HOME.

HMM. IT STILL GIVES ME A FUNNY FEELING — DON'T KNOW WHY.

Later, outside —

LOOK OUT, JUDY — A SLATE'S FALLEN OFF OUR ROOF!

THAT'S WEIRD. DAD ONLY INSPECTED THE ROOF AT THE WEEKEND — AND IT WAS ALL RIGHT THEN. THE DOLL COULDN'T HAVE HAD ANYTHING TO DO WITH IT, COULD IT?

DON'T, JOHN — YOU'RE FRIGHTENING ME!

Back at Judy's —

MUM, D'YOU THINK YOU COULD MAKE SOME CLOTHES FOR VICTORIA?

YES, I'LL SEE WHAT I CAN DO. BUT YOU'LL HAVE TO HELP, MIND.

ER — MUM — A SLATE FELL OFF JOHN'S ROOF AND ALMOST HIT ME. JOHN THINKS THE DOLL COULD HAVE HAD SOMETHING TO DO WITH IT.

OH, WHAT NONSENSE!

THAT LAD'S GOT TOO ACTIVE AN IMAGINATION FOR HIS OWN GOOD. IF SLATES FALL OFF A ROOF IT'S 'COS THE ROOF'S NOT PROPERLY MAINTAINED.

SUPPOSE YOU'RE RIGHT, DAD.

WHOSE DOLL WERE YOU THEN, EH? DON'T SUPPOSE I'LL EVER KNOW.

In the middle of the night —

WHAT THE — ? I — I THOUGHT I HEARD SOMEONE CRYING — A LITTLE GIRL.

Next day —

MUM AND DAD DIDN'T HEAR IT — BUT I'M SURE I DIDN'T IMAGINE IT.

I BELIEVE YOU. AND THAT'S THE SECOND STRANGE THING THAT'S HAPPENED SINCE YOU GOT THAT DOLL. WHY DON'T YOU GET RID OF IT?

I COULDN'T PART WITH VICTORIA. THERE MUST BE A SIMPLE EXPLANATION FOR THOSE OTHER THINGS.

Suddenly —

LOOK OUT, EVERYONE — THAT LORRY'S OUT OF CONTROL!

Desperately, they dived out of the way!

CRIKEY! TH — THAT WAS CLOSE!

SORRY ABOUT THAT, KIDS. MY BRAKES FAILED COMPLETELY COMING DOWN THAT HILL. STRANGE, 'COS THEY'RE WORKING NOW.

YOU HEAR THAT, JUDY?

THAT'S THE SECOND TIME THAT DOLL'S TRIED TO KILL YOU. C'MON, WE'RE GOING ROUND TO YOUR PLACE TO HAVE A GOOD LOOK AT IT!

HUH! CAN'T FIND ANYTHING ODD ABOUT IT.

'COURSE NOT — 'COS THERE ISN'T. WHAT DID YOU EXPECT TO FIND — HORNS AND A TAIL?

IT'S NO JOKE, JUDY. YOU'RE IN TERRIBLE DANGER.

That night —

OH, NO! IT'S THAT LITTLE GIRL'S VOICE AGAIN — SHE'S CRYING IN PAIN! OH, STOP — PLEASE!

Next morning, when John called round —

SHE — SHE WAS CRYING ALL NIGHT. THEN A FEW HOURS AGO SHE FELL ASLEEP. WE CAN'T WAKE HER. THE DOCTOR'S WITH HER NOW. THINKS SHE'S IN SOME SORT OF COMA.

SHE'LL HAVE TO GO TO HOSPITAL. THOUGH I DON'T KNOW WHAT THEY'LL DO. IT'S A VERY STRANGE CASE —

WHAT DO YOU MEAN?

WELL, THE ONLY OTHER TIME I'VE SEEN SOMEONE LIKE THIS WAS IN AFRICA. YOU HAVEN'T COME BACK FROM THERE BY ANY CHANCE?

NO. WE'VE NEVER BEEN ABROAD AT ALL.

HMM. VERY ODD . . .

Meanwhile, John had gone to the demolition site where Judy's Dad had been working —

NOT MUCH CHANCE OF FINDING ANY CLUES THERE, THEN.

'FRAID THAT RUBBLE'S ALL THAT'S LEFT OF THE HOUSE WHERE HE FOUND THE DOLL.

John was about to go home, when —

I CAN TELL YOU A FEW THINGS ABOUT THAT DOLL. BUT WHAT'S IT WORTH?

A — A GIRL'S LIFE COULD DEPEND ON IT.

John blurted out the whole story —

SORRY, LAD. DIDN'T REALISE. WELL, MY DAD WAS BORN ROUND THESE PARTS. PEOPLE TALKED THEN ABOUT THE LITTLE GIRL AND HER DOLL . . .

. . . SEEMS WAY BACK IN VICTORIAN TIMES, HER FATHER CAME BACK FROM AFRICA — AND BROUGHT HER THE DOLL AS A PRESENT. BUT THEN, WITHIN DAYS, SHE FELL ILL — AND DIED.

THE OLD WOMEN BLAMED THE DOLL — SAID IT WAS BEWITCHED AND LOOKS LIKE HER PARENTS THOUGHT SO, TOO. WHY ELSE BRICK IT UP LIKE THAT?

John rushed back to Judy's —

SO YOU SEE — THERE IS SOMETHING EVIL ABOUT THAT DOLL.

CALM YOURSELF, LAD. THAT'S JUST A LOAD OF OLD SUPERSTITIOUS NONSENSE. AND I'LL PROVE IT TO YOU —

SEE! JUDY'S FINE NOW.

HELLO, JOHN. FANCY A WALK WITH VICTORIA AND ME?

ARE YOU SURE YOU'RE ALL RIGHT, NOW?

OF COURSE, I AM — SO LONG AS VICTORIA STAYS WITH ME. AND SHE WILL — FOREVER!

C — CAN I HOLD VICTORIA FOR A MOMENT, JUDY?

NO, GET AWAY FROM ME! YOU WANT TO HURT VICTORIA — I WON'T LET YOU!

OH, NO — THE PAIN! VICTORIA — HELP ME! PLEASE, HELP ME! AAAGH!

Soon —

I — I'M FRIGHTENED. SHE'S IN THAT COMA AGAIN.

HOW DID IT HAPPEN, JOHN?

LOOK, GET THAT NONSENSE OUT OF YOUR HEAD.

I — I TRIED TO TAKE THE DOLL AWAY FROM HER. SHE WENT CRAZY — CRIED OUT IN PAIN, THEN FAINTED. THE DOLL'S EVIL — YOU'VE GOT TO BELIEVE ME.

But John knew it wasn't nonsense. He went to the local reference library, and looked up old newspaper files...

HERE IT IS — AN ARTICLE ABOUT THAT LITTLE GIRL AND HER DOLL . . . CRIKEY! THIS MUST CONVINCE JUDY'S DAD!

EVERYTHING THAT'S HAPPENED TO JUDY HAPPENED TO THE GIRL WHO HAD THE DOLL BEFORE — THE ACCIDENTS, HEARING CRYING IN THE MIDDLE OF THE NIGHT, THE STRANGE COMA — EVERYTHING.

HMM. MAYBE THERE IS SOMETHING IN ALL THIS, AFTER ALL. I'LL TAKE A LOOK AT THE DOLL.

THE AMBULANCE IS ON ITS WAY. I HOPE IT'S QUICK — SHE'S GETTING WEAKER.

HEY, THERE'S SOMETHING IN HERE!

SO THAT'S WHY IT KEPT REPEATING THE SAME WORDS — THIS WAS JAMMED IN THE MECHANISM. IT — IT'S A LITTLE WOODEN DOLL WITH A KNIFE IN ITS HEART!

When the doctor arrived, he recognised the doll immediately —

IT'S A VOODOO DOLL. I'VE SEEN THEM BEFORE — IN AFRICA! EVERYTHING FITS INTO PLACE NOW.

AFRICA? THE LITTLE GIRL'S FATHER HAD BEEN IN AFRICA!

SEEMS SOMEONE PUT A CURSE ON HIS LITTLE GIRL.

AND — AND THE CURSE IS STILL WORKING — ON OUR JUDY!

BUT WHAT CAN WE DO TO STOP THE CURSE ON JUDY?

SIMPLE — WE DESTROY THE VOODOO DOLL . . . BUT IF IT HADN'T BEEN FOR THIS YOUNG LAD, WE'D HAVE BEEN TOO LATE TO SAVE JUDY.

B — BUT WHAT IF IT DOESN'T WORK?

IT'S GOT TO — IT'S GOT TO!

As soon as the doll was burned, Judy woke up —

ER — HERE'S SOME FLOWERS, JUDY.

OH, JOHN, THANK YOU. BUT HAVE I BEEN ILL OR SOMETHING?

IT'S FUNNY — BUT I DON'T SEEM TO REMEMBER ANY-THING THAT'S HAPPENED TO ME IN THE LAST FEW DAYS . . . HEY, WHAT A LOVELY DOLL!

YEAH, AND IT'S GOT QUITE A STORY BEHIND IT!

REALLY? IT LOOKS A BIT SOPPY TO ME!

119

BOX OF TRICKS!

Here's a clever little box, ideal for putting something in to please any member of your family — playing cards for Dad, mints for Grandpa, tissue hankies for Grandma, draughts for a big brother, recipe cards for Mum — or counters and dice for a junior games-player, as shown in our photograph!

You only need an old box with a separate lid — we used an unwanted handerchief box — but you'll find a box used for chocolates, soap or any sort of cardboard presentation case will do nicely. Some Con-Tact sticky-back plastic, which you can buy from Woolworth's and most Do-it-Yourself shops is also required. Of course, the amount of Con-Tact you'll need will depend on how large you make the box, but, generally speaking ¼ — ½ yard of Con-Tact in two toning colours is ample.

To make the counters-box shown in our picture, first lay one piece of Cont-tact on a flat surface with the backing paper facing upwards. Place the box on top, and draw around with a margin of twice the depth of the box. Then cut this out with sharp scissors and remove the backing paper carefully, before laying the Con-Tact flat on the table with the sticky side up.

Now put the box in the centre of the Con-Tact piece and press down to make sure that the Con-Tact is stuck firmly to the bottom. And, at each corner, snip from the edge of the Con-Tact to the corner of the box, thus removing a square. You will then be able to fold the Con-Tact up and over the sides into the box, without problems.

Next, place the box on the first colour Con-Tact once more, and draw around to the exact size (without any margin). Remove backing paper, as before, and stick this piece of Con-Tact down carefully on the inside of the box

Cover the lid of the box in exactly the same way, using a contrasting colour of Con-Tact, if you want to. And, for the squared "draughts-box" look which you can see in our photograph, simply cut out small squares of contrasting Con-Tact and arrange them as you wish. Easy, isn't it?

If you want to make a games-size draughts board lid, perhaps using a box which once housed a discarded game, jigsaw puzzle or Christmas crackers, you will find that, by making your squared design with suede-look Con-Tact, the draughts will stay in place more easily when a game is in progress.

And don't just throw away the odd scraps of Con-Tact which are left. Stuck together, or on either side of a sheet of cardboard cut from an old washing-powder box or cereal packet, then cut into circles, they make lovely counters to go inside the box!

BESSIE BUNTER

HERE'S MY "MASTERPIECE" OF MY MISTRESS.

BESSIE OVERHEARD MISS STACKPOLE, HEAD OF CLIFF HOUSE, TALKING TO A JUNIOR MISTRESS...

THE FAMOUS ARTIST, PICASSO, HAS MADE A FORTUNE FROM HIS PAINTINGS! THERE'S CERTAINLY MONEY IN ART!

AND I COULD DO WITH SOME! I'LL START RIGHT AWAY!

WHILE COOK'S TALKING TO THE BREAD MAN, I'LL GRAB SOMETHING TO PAINT!

THE JELLY WAS THERE A MINUTE AGO, AND NOW...

FIND BESSIE BUNTER!

I THOUGHT YOU WERE SUPPOSED TO PAINT A STILL-LIFE SUBJECT, BESSIE!

THE TROUBLE WAS, IT WOULDN'T KEEP STILL! IT KEPT WOBBLING ALL OVER THE PLACE, UNTIL IT FINISHED UP—

I KNOW WHERE THAT JELLY FINISHED UP! TAKE AWAY HER EASEL AND SMOCK AT ONCE!

A PROMISING CAREER BLIGHTED BEFORE IT'S STARTED!

I KNOW! I'M GOING TO BE A LIGHTNING SKETCH ARTIST OUTSIDE CLIFF HOUSE!

OF COURSE YOU MAY MAKE A SKETCH OF ME! CARRY ON!

I'LL DASH THIS OFF IN A JIFFY!

FIFTY PENCE AND IT'S YOURS!

GAAAHH!

LUMME! NOW SHE'S DASHING OFF!

NOT TO WORRY! I'LL USE MY BOX OF PAINTS AND BECOME A "PAVEMENT PICASSO!"

HURRAH! SOMEBODY KNOWS ARTISTIC GENIUS WHEN THEY COME ACROSS IT!

MY HEAD

ANIMAL
MAGIC

Wee Sue

Sue Strong was up to her neck in grease and spanners preparing for the annual cycle safety competition...

THERE, THAT SHOULD DO IT. TIP-TOP SHAPE FOR THE BIG COMPETITION.

A MECHANICALLY SOUND BIKE IS ALL PART OF THE ART OF CYCLING.

LIKE RIDING DOWN THE HIGH STREET CAREFULLY, BACK STRAIGHT AND GIVING THE PROPER SIGNALS...

...THEN BENDING LOW OVER THE BARS TO ZAP DOWN THE BACK DOUBLES! YAHOO!

THAT CAR – IF SHE DOESN'T MOVE SOON...

OH DEAR, MY ENGINE'S CUT OUT!

I-I'VE SKIDDED STRAIGHT INTO IT – AAH!

HEAVENS ABOVE – A HI-JACK!

MY NEW CAR – IT'S BATTERED, BRUISED, SCRATCHED, DENTED...

HOW D'YOU FEEL, SUE?

LIKE A HEDGEHOG – THANKS TO THAT ROAD-HOG!

ER, YOUR CAR STALLED, MISS? LIKE ME TO HAVE A LOOK AT IT?

DON'T YOU DARE TOUCH IT! YOU'VE DONE ENOUGH DAMAGE TO MY POOR CAR AS IT IS!

THERE'LL BE NO ROAD SAFETY COMPETITION FOR YOU THIS DAY. IF YOU WERE A CAR DRIVER YOU'D BE BANNED FROM GOING ON THE ROAD, AND AS FAR AS I'M CONCERNED, YOU'RE BANNED FROM TAKING THAT BIKE INTO OR NEAR THE SCHOOL!

CRIKEY – OLD BIGGER TALKED HERSELF TO A STANDSTILL!

TALKING OF STANDSTILLS – I WISH SHE'D GET THE CARBURATION ON HER CAR FIXED – THE ENGINE'S TICKING-OVER TOO FAST.

The competition was in a nearby town . . .

NEVER MIND SUE, YOU CAN TAKE PART NEXT YEAR, YOUR BIKE'LL BE MENDED BY THEN!

YEAH, BUT I WAS REALLY LOOKING FORWARD TO IT TODAY.

ONE GOOD THING ABOUT MISS BIGGER GETTING A NEW CAR IS THAT SHE INSISTS ON GOING EVERYWHERE IN IT. SHE'S DRIVING TO THE ROAD SAFETY COMPETITION, SO WE GET TO TRAVEL ALONE AND HAVE A BIT OF FUN!

I'D LIKE TO HAVE SEEN MISS BIGGER'S FACE WHEN SUE RAN INTO HER PRECIOUS CAR!

BETTER NOT SAY TOO MUCH ABOUT IT. SUE'S IN A REAL BLACK MOOD AND SHE DOES SOME FUNNY THINGS WHEN SHE'S LIKE THAT.

I DIDN'T THINK SUE'D TAKE IT LIKE THIS. SHE DOESN'T LET THESE THINGS GET HER DOWN, USUALLY!

Ten minutes later . . .

MOVE OUT – LEMME AT IT!

DON'T HIT ME! YOU CAN USE MY BIKE!

SHE'S BEEN WATCHING TOO MANY FILMS!

HECK! THE DRIVER'S SLAMMED THE BRAKES ON!

SHE'S OBVIOUSLY FED-UP WITH US – SHE'S REALLY LAYING IT ON THE LINE.

THIS IS NO TIME TO JOKE! WE'VE GOT TO STOP HER BEFORE SHE GETS HURT.

HELLO, MISS BIGGER, I SEE YOU'VE STALLED AGAIN. NOT HAD A VERY GOOD TRACK RECORD WITH THIS CAR, HAVE YOU?

OH, MY GOODNESS – EXPRESS – SEVENTY MILES AN HOUR – JUST STOPPED – OH, MY GOODNESS!